OVERCOMING
ANXIETY

From Short-Term Fixes to Long-Recovery

RENEAU Z PEURIFOY, M.A.

LifeSkills Publications
Citrus Heights, California

Cover by GusTyk (caktyk@gmail.com)
Interior and eBook versions by JOSEP Book Designs (joseworkwork@gmail.com)
Photo of Mr. Peurifoy by Jessica Giblin

Second Edition © Copyright 2018 by Reneau Peurifoy,
    All rights reserved
First Edition © Copyright 1997 by Reneau Peurifoy, All rights reserved

Library of Congress Cataloging-in-Publication Data
Peurifoy, Reneau Z.
Overcoming anxiety: from short-term fixes to long-term recovery
Reneau Z. Peurifoy

p. cm.
ISBN   978-0-929437-03-3 (pbk)
        978-0-929437-04-0 (ePub)
        978-0-929437-05-7 (Mobi)

1. Anger–Problems, popular works.
I. Title
RC531.P43 1997   96-29376
616.85'223-dc20   CIP

CONTENTS

Author's Note ix

Preface xi

Acknowledgments xiii

Chapter 1: A New Way of Looking at Anxiety.....................1
    What Is Long-Term Recovery? 3
    How to Get the Most out of this Program 5

Chapter 2: The Imprint of Childhood.............................. 14
    Mary.. 15
    Robert 18
    Kimberly 22

Chapter 3: The Time Tunnel 27
    Conditioned Responses...27
    Posttraumatic Stress Disorder 28
    The Time Tunnel 32
    Escaping the Time Tunnel..33
    Four Common Traits in Adults with
        Abusive Childhoods 34

Chapter 4: The Mystery of Emotions 44
    What Are Emotions?..44
    Why Do We Have Emotions? 47
    Human Needs 49
    Core Beliefs 51

Chapter 5: Developing Your Explanation for "Why" 59

    The Answer Is E 62

    Five Factors That Can Trigger Symptoms 65

    Mary's, Robert's, and Kimberly's Simple Explanations.. 70

Chapter 6: Symptom-Management Skills 80

    Cue-Controlled Relaxation Response........................... 81

    Breathing Techniques 82

    Coping Self-Statements... 85

    Externalization/Distraction 89

Chapter 7: Distorted Thinking 96

    Distorted Thinking 96

    Should/must thinking..97

    Circular Questioning...98

    Magnification/Minimization 101

    Negative Anticipation (What-if Thinking) and
        Emotional Reasoning 102

    Challenging Irrational and Negative Self-Talk 105

Chapter 8: Progressive Desensitization 112

    Developing a Plan.. 112

    Basic Guidelines for Practicing 116

    Examples 119

    Increased Suggestibility...123

**Chapter 9: Moving from Basic to Advanced Symptom
           Control** 129

    First Steps to Advanced Symptom Control..................129

    Confronting Death and Uncertainty 133

    Shame...136

Chapter 10: Establishing Healthy Boundaries 142

    What Are Boundaries in Human Relationships?......... 142

Missing Anxiety's Message..143
Holiday Anxiety 148
Honoring Your Rights 149
The Excessive Need for Approval...............................150
Summary Sheets 152

Chapter 11: Detours along the Path to Recovery 160
Practice, Practice, Practice 160
Relearning Is Easier Than Starting from Scratch 165
More Bumps along the Road to Long-Term Recovery. 170
D.E.R. Scripts...171
Honoring Your Responsibility to Respect the
    Rights of Others..174
Unexpected Anger When Practicing Assertive Skills... 176

Chapter 12: Two Important "Quiet" Messages 180
Quiet Message One: Learn to Manage
    Periods of High Stress..180
Quiet Message Two: Find a Source
    of Spiritual Strength 183
Developing a Message Checklist 185

Chapter 13: Viewing Yourself in a New Way 191
What Makes Me Valuable? 194
Perfectionism 198
Exaggerating the Importance of Mistakes...................200
Learning to "Normalize" Yourself...............................201

Chapter 14: Final Steps 205
Where Do I Go from Here?...206
What If I'm Feeling Stuck? 207
Applying Your Skills to Other Areas of Your Life........208
A Final Word..210

Appendix 1: Guidelines for Selecting a Therapist 211

Appendix 2: Locating a Self-Help Group 216

Appendix 3: Suggestions for Better Sleep 219

Appendix 4: How to Develop a Relaxation Response 227

About the Author 231

Additional Books by Reneau Peurifoy 233

Connect with Reneau Peurifoy 237

AUTHOR'S NOTE

The ideas, procedures, and suggestions in this book are not intended as a substitute for consulting with either a physician or a psychotherapist. You should regularly consult a physician in matters relating to your health, particularly with respect to any symptoms that may require diagnosis or medical attention. Likewise, if you are finding it difficult to cope with daily life or stressful events, you are urged to seek help from a qualified psychotherapist.

PREFACE

Preface to the First Edition (1997)

In 1988, I completed work on my first book, *Anxiety, Phobias, and Panic: Taking Charge and Conquering Fear*, and became the first person to present an integrated, "multi-modal" treatment approach at a national conference on anxiety. In the years that followed, this approach became the standard course of treatment for people working with anxiety, and *Anxiety, Phobias, and Panic* became the book of choice among individuals, treatment facilities, therapists, and self-help groups working with anxiety both in the United States and in Europe.

As I completed revisions for the updated second edition of *Anxiety, Phobias, and Panic* in 1992, I knew that, as good as it was, something more was needed. In conversations with therapists and leaders of self-help groups nationwide, I became increasingly aware that while the treatment models being used were providing relief from anxiety, they were not enough. Like many other therapists, I was focusing more and more in my own practice on helping people move beyond the initial stages of symptom control to what I called long-term recovery.

As a result, I began working on this book in 1993 with the goal that it would move beyond my first work, break new ground, and show people suffering from anxiety how to achieve long-term recovery. After completing an outline and four chapters, I had to delay work on the initial draft for a year and a half to work on another project. This delay helped me develop the ideas that had been roughed out with numerous clients and has made the final work much more mature.

Because this book focuses on achieving long-term recovery and the "messages" behind anxiety, it presents the "basics" of symptom control in a simplified manner. Readers who want a more detailed explanation of this aspect of managing anxiety will find it useful to refer to my first book, *Anxiety, Phobias, and Panic*.

It is my hope that the struggles and victories of the people described in this book will help you live a fuller and more satisfying life. If you take the time to follow their example, I sincerely believe that you will succeed in your struggle with anxiety and achieve long-term recovery.

Preface to the Second Edition (2018)

It's been twenty years since the first edition of this book was published, and it's been gratifying to see what is now called "relapse prevention" become part of the standard treatment model used by therapists working with Anxiety Disorders. In this book, I will continue to use the term "long-term recovery" as it more accurately captures the idea of freeing oneself from the lies and habit patterns that once held you in chains.

I have revised this edition to reflect what has been learned since the first edition was published and to make it even more user-friendly. My continued hope is that you find it useful in achieving your own long-term recovery.

ACKNOWLEDGMENTS

This book would have been impossible if not for the hundreds of people who shared their lives with me. Thank you for the insights you have given me and the help that my work with you will provide the readers of this book.

Laura DaLanni, Sandra Festian, Nancy Flocchini, Jane Hoff, John Marzo, Lynn Maguire, Debbie Roth, and Kay Stathacopoulos, read the original draft and gave many suggestions for additions and changes. Alissyn Link went through the second draft and helped shape it into its final form. Two others who helped with the first edition include Rita Clark who recommended two of the above readers and Shirley Green, the founder of Agoraphobics Building Independent Lives (ABIL) who has been a great source of encouragement over the years.

I would also like to thank my wife, Michiyo, who has patiently stood by my side while I gained the experience and knowledge necessary to write this book.

As I finalized the second edition, Pheshwriter did an excellent job as copyeditor.

Finally, I would like to thank my parents. Without them I would not be who I am today. I dedicate this book to them.

CHAPTER 1

A New Way of Looking at Anxiety

Since I first began working with anxiety-related problems in 1981, there has been an explosion of knowledge about their causes and treatments. Today, there's a flood of books and videos that describe programs for overcoming anxiety-related problems as well as an increasing number of centers and therapists who specialize in treating them. In addition, Research has shown that the approaches currently being used to treat anxiety-related problems do work, provide relief, and help many achieve a life free from debilitating anxiety.

In spite of the tremendous progress that has been made, there are still too many who go to a specialist or work through a self-help program and experience good initial results, but, after a period of time that can range from a few weeks to many years, they do find that their symptoms return. For some, the symptoms return in full force with debilitating anxiety and panic attacks and the redevelopment of avoidance behaviors or rituals. For others, the symptoms return at a level that is lower than originally experienced or reemerge in a somewhat different form such as excessive worry or nervousness. They might also develop avoidance behavior or nervous rituals that are different from those that accompanied the original onset of debilitating anxiety.

There are also some who find that while treatment greatly reduces their initial symptoms, they continue to experience a significant level of anxiety-related symptoms. When anxiety symptoms return, or are never fully resolved, the sense of failure, anger, confusion, and depression that occurs can be overwhelming.

In this book, you'll meet three people who have achieved long-term recovery. You'll see how each battled the crippling effects of severe anxiety, and won. Their battle was not an easy one nor was it over quickly. As you read about how they accomplished this, you'll learn many new things about yourself, gain many new skills, and develop a new way of looking at anxiety.

One of the central themes of this book is that anxiety is simply a "messenger" that is telling you that you have one or more important life issues to address. Sometimes, symptoms develop because a person is overwhelmed by too many things going on at the same time, such as problems with health, money, children, or work. However, anxiety can also be connected with problems in relationships (such as your ability to connect and be intimate with others) as well as with what are often called "existential" issues (how we answer questions such as: "What is the meaning of life?" and "How do I find happiness?"). These types of things can also become intertwined with a medical condition such as an adverse reaction to a medication or a traumatic experience such as a terrible car accident to produce the panic-anxiety cycle.

The purpose of this book is to help you understand the message your symptoms is sending to you. All too often, it's easy to become so focused on the symptoms of anxiety (the messenger) that you fail to understand the message (the true cause). While the message that anxiety represents is sometimes difficult to face, identifying it lifts the feeling of shame and demoralization that develops when you're focused on the elimination of the symptoms. It's also the key to achieving what I call long-term recovery.

Once this idea is accepted, the goal shifts from an absence of anxiety to experiencing anxiety as a normal part of the challenges that life brings. This is a more reasonable goal. Once the focus becomes the message (the underlying issues generating the anxiety) rather than the messenger (the symptoms), long-term recovery is possible.

What Is Long-Term Recovery?

Long-term recovery is really the final stage of the process that people who recover fully from debilitating anxiety go through. As people move through this process, they achieve progressively higher levels of recovery. For the sake of simplicity, I've divided these into the following three levels:

Level One: Basic Symptom Control

At this stage of recovery, intense anxiety is being experienced. Because of this, the focus is on symptom control. This is understandable. When you're experiencing intense symptoms, you aren't interested in long-term answers. You want relief and you want it NOW!

By the end of this stage, however, much improvement has been made. Anxiety symptoms are reduced with only occasional episodes of intense anxiety or panic, and there is usually the ability to function comfortably in at least half of the everyday situations that were formerly uncomfortable.

There is also a good understanding of the mechanisms of anxiety, along with a broad range of coping skills for managing symptoms. While no longer hypervigilant (always on guard, watching for symptoms), people at this stage are still moderately on guard. For many, medication continues to play a major role in symptom management.

Level Two: Advanced Symptom Control

People at this stage of recovery are gaining greater confidence in their skills due to the absence of most, if not all, avoidance behavior. Intense episodes of anxiety are now infrequent. To at least a moderate degree, they have come to terms with those aspects of their personality that can cause problems and, when present, the genetic predisposition that makes them prone to anxiety. They have gotten to the point where, for the most part, they will not let symptoms interfere with their behavior. They know how to avoid the anxiety-panic cycle and use their various skills effectively. There is some understanding that symptoms are messengers.

Those at this stage who relied heavily on medication at level one are now no longer using medication, using it at a reduced level, or reserving its use for situations that are especially anxiety provoking such as a long flight.

Although anxiety is still a fearful thing, there is now more awareness of the issues that trigger anxiety. The focus has shifted, at least in part, away from the symptoms to the causes of anxiety. However, because this understanding is incomplete, periodic flare-ups of moderate to intense symptoms still occur. When this happens, there is a tendency to move back to level one and again become preoccupied with symptoms and develop avoidance behaviors.

Level Three: Long-Term Recovery

People at this level perceive anxiety in a completely different way from those at level one or two. Anxiety is now seen as a natural part of life rather than as something to be avoided. They can easily identify their core issues and understand clearly and fully the various messages anxiety sends. When anxiety is experienced, they realize that high levels of anxiety are supposed to occur when difficult real-life issues are present, so the focus becomes addressing the issues generating the anxiety rather than the symptoms of anxiety. This, in turn, allows them to experience high levels of anxiety without the distress or escalation of symptoms experienced when their anxiety-related problems began. Those at this stage who formerly relied on medication for symptom control, find it no longer needed.

Before proceeding, take a moment to decide which of the above levels best describes you at this time. If this is the first book you've read on anxiety, you may still be caught in the initial intense symptoms and have yet to experience any relief. If you've battled anxiety for years, you've probably read many books, been through one or more programs, or seen several therapists in your quest for recovery. During this time, you may have cycled back and forth between level one and two. In either case, my goal is to give you the tools and the knowledge you need to achieve long-term recovery.

How to Get the Most out of this Program

This book is designed to be used as a workbook. In order to get the most out of it, you need to read through it slowly; I suggest you spend at least one week on each chapter and do as many of the recommended activities as possible. While it's best to work through the book slowly, some people just can't wait to learn what's in each chapter. If you are one of these, go ahead and read through the entire book to get a general idea of what it covers. Once you've done this, return to the beginning and work your way through the book slowly.

If you have read other books on anxiety disorders, gone through an anxiety treatment program or seen a therapist, it's likely that you have achieved some success in your struggle with anxiety. It's also likely that you will be familiar with some of the skills described in the earlier sections. While it may be tempting to rush through them to get to the material that may be new to you, don't be in too big of a hurry. There may be ideas that can help you use the skills you've learned more effectively.

In order to achieve the long-term recovery described in this chapter, you need more than just a general understanding of ideas. Your goal is to internalize the information and skills presented in each chapter and make them a natural and automatic part of your behavior. The recommended activities play a key role in this process. The more time and energy you spend on them, the more successful you will be.

Beginning with the next chapter, plan to spend at least one week on each chapter before you move on to the next one. Start by reading the headings to get an overview of the material. Then read the whole chapter at your usual reading rate. It's best to read each chapter at least three times, more if you find the information difficult. The second and third readings will increase your understanding of the material and reveal ideas that were missed during the first reading.

There may be times when you could spend more than one week on a chapter. While it is important to be thorough, it is also important to maintain your momentum. Therefore, spend no more than two weeks on a chapter, and do as many of the recommended activities as possible during that time. After completing the program, you can spend additional time on those areas where you feel more work is needed.

This may sound like a lot of work; it is. But keep in mind that it took your whole life to develop the behaviors and thinking patterns that produced your condition. It will take time, energy, and a strong commitment to learn the new ways of thinking and acting that lead to long-term recovery. If you work through the material in the manner outlined, chances are excellent that you will succeed.

Summary of Key Ideas

1. Anxiety is a normal part of life. It is a "messenger" that indicates the presence of a problem or issue that needs to be resolved. The more intense the anxiety, the more important the issue. People with severe anxiety often have important life issues they are not dealing with effectively.
2. Long-term recovery focuses on the management of anxiety as a natural part of life rather than on the absence of anxiety.
3. There are three different levels of recovery possible. Many people become stuck at the first or second level, or cycle back and forth between the first two levels.
4. People who achieve long-term recovery perceive anxiety differently from those at the first two levels of recovery. Their focus is on the issues generating the anxiety rather than the symptoms of anxiety.
5. Focusing on the message of anxiety allows them to experience high levels of anxiety without the distress or escalation of symptoms experienced when their anxiety-related problems began.
6. In order to achieve long-term recovery, you need to work through the program presented in this book in a slow and systematic manner.

Recommended Activities

Getting the Most out of the Recommended Activities

At the end of each chapter is a set of activities that many have found valuable in achieving long-term recovery. You may find that some of the activities involve information or skills you have already learned and are a part of how you usually think and act. Or, you may find that the material seems awkward, uncomfortable, or difficult. This is to be expected since this program is designed to meet the needs of a wide variety of people. You are unique, with your own personal requirements and abilities. So, spend less time with activities you find easy and more time with those that seem difficult.

The easy activities probably involve skills you have already practiced and ideas you have already internalized. The difficult ones probably involve skills and ideas that are new to you or that you've never really mastered. These are the ones that are the most important for you. However, if a particular activity causes undue stress or anxiety, it means you are not ready for it. Skip it and work on exercises that are less difficult. Then return to the stressful exercise later. After working in other areas, you will probably find that it is not as stressful as when you first tried it.

One of the keys to achieving long-term recovery is developing the ability to hear the message that your symptoms are sending. This is often difficult. So, even though a particular exercise may not seem like it applies to you, do it anyway. You may be surprised by the results.

No one can say exactly how long it will take you to achieve long-term recovery. It depends on your genetic make-up, your personality, and the complexity and difficulty of both the issues from your childhood and your present circumstances. It should also be noted that when you do achieve long-term recovery, you probably won't know it until you've been there for quite some time. This is the way personal growth takes place. However, if you have a strong commitment to use the book as it is designed—to do the reading and apply as many of the suggestions to your life as possible even though you may think they are silly or may not fully understand why they are suggested—it is very likely you will succeed.

Establish a Regular Study Time

As you work through this book, keep in mind that it is a self-directed study program. Establish a regular time to work with the activities at the end of the chapters, and make this scheduled study time as important as your regular meals. If you use a calendar or appointment book or app, record your study times in it. Having a regular study time helps you avoid the common mistake of working only when you are experiencing high levels of anxiety. Remember the "good day rule": You can make the most progress when you are feeling good and your life seems to be running smoothly. It's during these times that it's easiest to look at yourself objectively and do the activities listed in the chapters. It's also when you are least motivated to do them. Do them anyway. It is during your good days that you will be most able to develop the skills and understanding you need to achieve long-term recovery.

Write a Brief Explanation of Your Condition

Before you go on to the next chapter, write a brief explanation of why you think your symptoms developed and why they continue to be a problem. This explanation can range from one paragraph to a page in length. Keep this explanation so you can refer to it later.

Consider Using Supplemental Material

This book is designed to be used by itself. However, in many ways it is an extension of my first book, *Anxiety, Phobias, and Panic*. If you have not read any other books on anxiety, seen a therapist who specializes in anxiety or gone through a program for anxiety, you may find my first book to be a useful resource. Since the focus of this book is on the underlying messages that need to be heard in order to achieve long-term recovery, many of the basic skills only covered briefly. For example, the symptom management skills described in chapter 6 are presented in much more detail in my first book as are some of the other basic and intermediate skills presented in this one.

Consider Psychotherapy

Although many people have used the approach in this book to achieve long-term recovery without the help of a psychotherapist, others have found it best to use it in conjunction with professional psychotherapy. If you are experiencing extreme difficulty coping with life, find a therapist experienced in working with anxiety-related problems. Guidelines on how to select a therapist are given in appendix 1.

Find a Study Partner

Although it is possible to work through this book on your own, many find it helpful to have a friend or relative read and work through the material with them. Your study partner does not need to be a person with anxiety-related problems, but he or she does need to be someone you trust and with whom you are comfortable. Discussing the chapters with a study partner deepens your understanding. This partner will also be able to help you discover things in the material you may not see on your own.

Consider Joining a Self-Help Group

Many people find that a self-help group is tremendously useful in helping them to achieve long-term recovery. A well-run support group offers the advantages of a study partner multiplied by the number of people in the group. Appendix 2 describes how to find a local self-help group.

A Word about Medication

Most come to therapy seeking a quick and easy solution that will return them to where they were before their distressing symptoms began. This is a normal reaction and explains the heavy reliance on medication so common among anxiety sufferers. In response to this demand, a wide variety of medications have been developed that can reduce anxiety symptoms. While they can be very useful in stabilizing a person who is feeling out of control, they are often not the best long-term solution. About half the people I see were prescribed medication prior to coming to me. The others have either taken no medication or are using medication "as needed." Of the three case studies in this book, Mary was taking a tranquilizer as needed, Robert was on a regular dose of medication, and Kimberly was not taking any medication. Kimberly had taken medication in the past but discontinued using it prior to seeing me because she did not like the side effects it caused.

In each case, I told them what I usually tell those I'm working with. If you're taking medication, continue taking it as it has been prescribed. While most do not like being on medication, it's important to stay on any prescribed medication until you feel you've mastered the basic skills and are ready to begin reducing the dosage. If you decide to go off your medication, be sure to consult the physician who prescribed it, and go off gradually. If you've been taking medication regularly, the sudden withdrawal from it may cause an increase in your symptoms or produce other adverse effects.

If you're not taking medication and are able to function adequately, I encourage you to see what you can accomplish with the skills taught in this book. If your symptoms are making it difficult for you to function, then medication may help to reduce those symptoms enough so you can cope with life while you work through this book. If you decide to try medication, I would recommend that you see a psychiatrist rather than a family physician. Psychiatrists specialize in psychoactive medications (medications that affect emotions and mental processes) and are better able to select the medication for you and make adjustments if side effects occur. As with all physicians, seek a psychiatrist who listens carefully to you. The guidelines listed in appendix 1 for selecting a therapist also apply to psychiatrists.

One key exception to the above general guidelines is obsessive-compulsive disorder. Since this condition has a significant biological component, medication is often helpful when used in conjunction with a cognitive behavioral approach, such as the one described in this book.

A Word to the Significant Other of a Person with Anxiety-Related Problems

I strongly recommend that the significant other of a person with anxiety-related problems become educated about what his or her loved one is experiencing. Unfortunately, one's significant other is often fearful about or scornful toward his or her loved one's anxiety-related problems. Sometimes this is due to a secret fear that if the loved one gets better and becomes more independent, the relationship will end. Other times, it's because the significant other is dealing with issues that are similar to those of the loved one. Sometimes, simple ignorance as to the nature and causes of anxiety-related problems leads a significant other to view the loved one as being "silly" or "childish." The result is that the significant other withdraws and ignores the problem or tries to "fix" the loved one by giving simplistic solutions that do not help. Both of these approaches weaken the relationship and cause anger and bitterness in the person who is suffering from the anxiety-related problem.

As you educate yourself, you may find that you are dealing with many issues similar to those of your loved one. When this is the case, sharing such a discovery can be very beneficial. It can also help you become more effective in your own life. One of the best ways to educate yourself is to become a study partner. If your personality or your relationship with your loved one makes this difficult, you can at least read this book and discuss what you have learned.

I encourage you to do the exercises yourself and discuss those sections of the book that describe issues with which you struggle. For example, you can construct your own genogram as you work through chapter 2 and identify core beliefs and associations that interfere with your life as you work through chapter 5. Since much of what is written in this book applies to everyone, you may find that you and your loved one share many struggles of which you were unaware. Working through the book in this manner is a wonderful way to support your loved one and will probably deepen the bond between you.

CHAPTER 2

The Imprint of Childhood

In this chapter you'll meet Mary, Robert, and Kimberly. Each one struggled with anxiety and achieved long-term recovery. The road they traveled is similar to the road that many of the people I've worked with have taken, regardless of their diagnoses. Although the issues you're facing may be different from theirs, keep in mind that the purpose of following their journey is to extract principles that you can apply to your struggles. While doing this, you may find many areas in which their stories are similar to yours.

Each of the following descriptions of Mary, Robert, and Kimberly is divided into four sections. The first section gives a brief profile along with the initial description of the difficulties that person reported. This is followed by a genogram; this is a diagram of the various people in the person's family. The squares in each genogram represent males, and the circles represent females. A horizontal line represents a marriage. A vertical zig zag line (such as the one in Robert's and Kimberly's genograms) represents a divorce. The vertical lines drawn to Mary, Robert, and Kimberly are a little longer than those drawn to their brothers and sisters. This is simply to make them stand out from their siblings.

Siblings are listed from oldest to youngest. In the following genograms, Mary is the youngest child in her family, while Robert and Kimberly are both the oldest. In addition to their parents, the genograms include adults who played an active role in their lives while they grew up. In Mary's case, this included her parents, her maternal grandmother and grandfather, and her uncle. In Kimberly's case, this included her natural parents along with her step-father.

Following each genogram is a brief description of each adult and a set of early recollections from grade school, middle school, and high school years.

Mary

Mary is an attractive woman in her late twenties; about five feet four with a slender, athletic build. She is divorced and works as a secretary in a state government agency. During our first session, she said that she only experienced panic attacks a few times a month. However, high levels of anxiety and worry were part of her daily life. Mary had been battling anxiety for almost five years. She had seen a couple of therapists and had experienced some relief. Lately, however, her symptoms were again getting worse. She did not travel very far from where she lived, and usually avoided theaters, restaurants, and any social gatherings where more than two or three people were present.

Mary is a long distance runner but could no longer run in the foothills where she had loved to train in the past. She reported that her symptoms began while traveling when she was on an airplane during a storm. On her next flight, a short time later, she again experienced intense anxiety. After this, she began to experience panic attacks more frequently and in more situations. Her condition was initially diagnosed as panic disorder with agoraphobia.

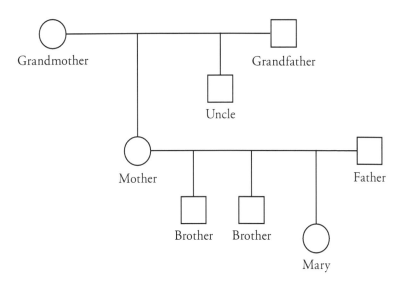

The Adults in Mary's Childhood

Mother: Mom was a secretary in my grade school. She was a very critical person and always seemed anxious. She has never driven at night, and I believe she's an alcoholic. She begins sipping wine around dinnertime and sort of "zones out" for the evening. She was fairly distant when I was young, but we've become somewhat closer as I've grown older.

Father: Dad was a truck driver, so he was gone a lot while I was growing up. He always seemed to be angry about something. He was an only child, and I think this is why he was fairly self-centered. I remember that he controlled the house. However, I think he was a good father. I knew he loved me even though he never said it, as he made sure we had whatever we needed. I was his "little princess" when I was young and couldn't wait for him to come home from his trips. I always wanted to please him. He took us to the park on Sunday, which became a high point for me throughout my younger years. As I got older we became more distant. I hardly talked to him at all after Middle School.

Grandfather: Grandfather was definitely an alcoholic. While I didn't know him very well, from what I've heard he was a very troubled man. He killed himself with poison. Unfortunately, he didn't take enough to kill himself quickly, and he suffered a long, miserable death. He was a nervous man. I've heard stories that he stopped driving when he was in his fifties. He told everyone that cars were just going too fast for him.

Grandmother: As with my grandfather, Grandmother was just sort of in the background. We would visit periodically and she would always be busy in the kitchen or cleaning something. I liked her because she always had a hug and something sweet for me to eat.

Uncle: My uncle came by every now and then. I remember that when he came we would go out to eat and have a good time. There was a lot of talking and joking. Dad seemed to like him a lot. I was always proud to tell everyone he was my Uncle Jake.

Mary's Early Recollections

Preschool through Grade School: I was terrified in the first few weeks of kindergarten. I don't remember why, but for some reasons I refused to tie my shoes throughout all of kindergarten. During grade school, I often thought my friends were talking about me and that they felt sorry for me. I would do anything to please my teachers. I felt unloved, and spent a lot of time playing with make-believe friends until about the first grade. I remember lots of punishment from Mom. She would spank or slap us and put Tabasco sauce or soap in my mouth whenever she thought I was "talking back." I was a "cry baby" and would cry over almost anything. My brothers teased and ridiculed me a lot. Sometimes they were very cruel. I felt like a burden to my mother because I once heard her saying that I was "unplanned." I can remember never feeling safe except when I would hide in the back of my closet and cover myself with dirty clothes.

Middle School: I became active in sports and found that this was an area where I could do well. I liked track and field, and began running. I had friends but none were really close friends. I always had the feeling of being on the outside looking in. I tended to devote my time to running and schoolwork. As a result, I did well in school.

High School: High school was more of the same. I continued to run, dated some, and had friends, but I always felt like I never really connected with anyone.

Early Adult: My marriage was fairly good during the early years. I was happy at last and felt like I had found my niche. Then, when the anxiety began, things started going downhill. At first, my husband tried to understand and was supportive. But, eventually I think he just got fed up with all of my worry and anxiety and decided to call it quits. We divorced about two years ago. Since there were no children we just split everything up and went our separate ways.

Robert

Robert had just turned forty when he came to our first session. He is about five feet six, married for the second time, and had one child, a son from his first marriage. Robert was experiencing extreme anxiety almost constantly. He was the supervisor of a very stressful unit in a manufacturing plant and was just barely able to function there. In addition to experiencing major panic attacks at work and very high levels of anxiety, he had an unusual gag response that prevented him from eating anything except soup and baby food.

Robert reported that his symptoms began four years earlier while he was on a business trip. He had a severe case of flu and happened to choke on some food in a restaurant. His initial diagnosis was also panic disorder because, like Mary, he was experiencing frequent panic attacks and avoidance patterns. Since doctors could find no medical reason for Robert's unusual gag response, and it seemed connected with the stress he was experiencing, a secondary tentative diagnosis of conversion disorder was also made. Conversion disorder refers to a physical response that is generated by psychological rather than physiological causes. Essentially, it's a representation of or a reaction to inner psychological conflict.

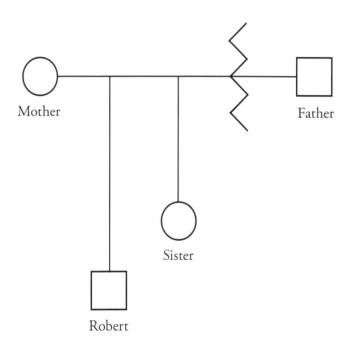

The Adults in Robert's Childhood

Mother: Mother was born in another country and married Dad while he was stationed overseas. She was a very emotional person. Sometimes she would explode and say how stupid I was whenever I or another family member did something that displeased her. Other times she would burst into tears. She had a very hard life when she was little and was not very well educated. She was a very negative person and not too close to us emotionally. She did not work outside of the home. In fact, her main focus in life was home. During high school, I thought of her as Alice in Wonderland because she seemed to live in her own little world and never really knew what was going on in the lives of the people around her. Our home always looked great and we were always well dressed and neat. Someone looking at us from the outside probably thought we were a great family because we always looked so good. She divorced my father after I left the house.

Father: Father was an electrical engineer. He was an alcoholic and drank several beers every night while sitting in front of the television. He would drink two or three six-packs on the weekend. It seemed like we were always running out of beer. Father was a very intense person who was often violent. About once a week he and Mother would get into an argument and he would end up hitting her. Sometimes he would hit us. I remember that everything had to be his way or no way. There was always a "correct" way to do everything.

Robert's Early Recollections

Preschool through Grade School: One of my earliest memories was when I was at dinner and started choking. I thought, "I can't let anyone see this." Father saw I was having trouble and helped me dislodge the piece of food that was stuck in my throat by slapping me on the back. Afterward, no one said anything and they just went on with dinner as if nothing had happened. I wasn't very happy as a kid and was always on edge. At night I was often afraid of being beaten by Father. We lived outside of the United States during most of my younger years. I was in Indiana when I was two. First grade was spent in Pakistan, then, we came back to the states for a while. From the fourth grade through middle school we lived in Japan. During the time that we lived overseas, I was picked on by bullies at school and lived in constant fear that they would beat me. In order to appear strong, I always hid how I felt.

Middle School: This was a terrible time in my life. I was very small, and several bullies in the class made beating me up their purpose in life. I had few friends. Academically, I was an average student and got B's and C's.

High School: I was still the smallest kid in my high school. However, we were now living in the United States, so I seemed to fit in better. I developed a circle of friends and continued to be an average student with Bs and Cs.

Early Adult: Nothing too outstanding happened to me. I went to college and got a business administration degree. My first marriage lasted ten years and was fairly rocky. I followed my father's pattern and was quite the bully in the early years of my first marriage. Although I changed a lot during those ten years, my wife remained full of bitterness because of the early years. I don't think she ever saw the changes I made. We finally divorced but stayed on reasonable terms because of our son. We both want to do what's right for him, so we communicate well in that area. I met my second wife at work and the marriage would be great if it weren't for this problem I have with choking. It's creating a lot of tension between us.

Kimberly

Kimberly was tall, around six feet, a somewhat heavy woman, in her late thirties with a very effervescent personality. Divorced and with two sons who live with her, Kimberly works as a school district nurse helping disabled students with severe medical and emotional problems. As we talked, she told me how, about six months earlier, she had been attacked by one of the students under her care. She talked about how during the assault she was hurt severely, and was now having intense episodes of anxiety during the day and nightmares of the incident at night. She was always "on guard" and avoided parks, convenience stores and many other places where she feared she might be attacked.

Kimberly took a medical leave for about a month after the incident and then an unpaid leave because she felt she could not go back. She was initially diagnosed as having posttraumatic stress disorder.

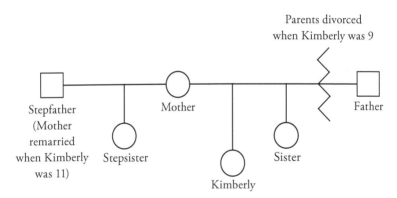

The Adults in Kimberly's Childhood

Mother: Mother was a beautician/hairdresser. She was a beautiful woman and an excellent mom. Our home was always neat and clean. She was always there for us when we needed anything for school. She was easy to talk to and we have always been close.

Father: Father was a high school P.E. teacher. He was kind of like a drill sergeant: demanding, unforgiving, dogmatic, and a perfectionist. Nothing ever seemed to please him. I never had any real relationship with him. We were always competing. We were an active family and did lots of outdoor activities like fishing, basketball, volleyball, and so on. However, there was always this fierce competition to see who would get the biggest fish or win a game. He never said, "I love you," and there was never any real demonstration of love. I continued to see my birth father after Mother remarried and I loved him very much. However, our relationship has always been one long contest.

Step-Father: My stepfather managed a large chain grocery store. He was friendly and much more even tempered than my birth father. We got along well, and by the time I entered high school I was much closer to him than to my birth father. He was a real anchor for me during my teenage years.

Kimberly's Early Recollections

Preschool through Grade School: My childhood was good. I was happy and had lots of friends. I liked school and did well, getting Bs and As. We were a very active family. We played all kinds of sports and went camping at least twice a year. There were no major traumas during childhood —just this constant competition with my father. I think he was disappointed at having only girls. I think that's why I was so into sports. It was a way for me to connect with Dad and my large size helped me compete. The only negative note was that Dad was so hard to please. I think I made up for it by becoming closer to my mother.

Middle School: For the most part, I enjoyed middle school. I continued to be active in sports. However, it's difficult being tall at this age. I was five feet eight inches in the seventh grade and was self-conscious about my height, especially around boys who were so much shorter than I was. I was a good student who got Bs and As. My size made me a great competitor in sports.

High School: I became less active in sports and turned more of my attention toward academics and drama. I loved to sing and did very well in school. By the tenth grade, there were enough boys I knew in my grade or grades above mine who were as tall as I was so that I wasn't feeling like such a freak anymore. However, I did get a lot of ribbing and heard all of the tall jokes that have ever been thought of. All in all, however, I had a pretty good time in high school.

Early Adult: I enjoyed nursing school even though it was difficult. I met my husband and we had three girls fairly early in our marriage. I worked part-time when they were small. I began working full-time at my current position in the school district about six years ago and have always felt like I was making a real contribution. Until the assault, I was never worried about the kids and felt like I could handle anything.

Even a cursory glance at the brief descriptions above suggests that Mary, Robert, and Kimberly each carried baggage from childhood into adulthood. As each talked about his or her childhood experiences, it became even more evident.

Summary of Key Ideas

1. A good way to take an objective look at childhood influences in your life is to construct a genogram that shows all of the adults who were significant during your childhood.
2. After creating the genogram, write a brief description of each adult. Then record early recollections of grade school, middle school, high school and your early adult years.

3. As you follow the stories of Mary, Robert, and Kimberly in the following chapters, look for principles you can apply to your struggle with anxiety.

Recommended Activities

Construct a Genogram of Your Family

Using the models presented in this chapter, construct a genogram that shows your family when you were young. Just as Mary included her maternal grandmother, be sure to include grandparents, uncles, aunts, and anyone else who played a significant role during your developmental years. If you're in a close relationship with someone, make a second genogram of this person and his or her family. Use a full sheet of eight-and-a-half-by-eleven inch paper to do this so you can include everyone who was in your life when you were young on the same sheet.

Write Descriptions of Your Parents

After you've completed your genogram, write a description of each adult who played a significant role in your life. You can either do this on the sheet with the genogram or on a separate sheet. Include a few words about their personalities. Were they easygoing, shy, critical, or outgoing? Also, include a few words about your relationship with them. Was it warm or cold, were they easy to talk to or distant? Some find it helpful to pretend that they are writing a character description for someone who is going to play the role of that person in a movie.

Write Descriptions of Your Early Experiences

After you've completed your descriptions of the adults in your life when young, write a brief description of what it was like when you were very young (earliest memories through the sixth grade); during your middle school years (seventh through ninth grade); high school (tenth through twelfth grade); and early adult years (after graduating from twelfth grade). Do not focus only on what is positive or negative. Instead, list ordinary recollections. The goal is to paint a portrait of what life was like for you in general during each of these periods of time.

CHAPTER 3

The Time Tunnel

M
ost of the people I've worked with spend a lot of time puzzling over why they are struggling with anxiety. Questions such as, "Why did this happen?" "What's wrong with me?" or "Why can't I just get over this?" occupy many of their waking hours. Because of this, it's important to have a reasonable and understandable answer for these "whys." Having an answer allows you to focus on learning how to reduce your symptoms and move toward long-term recovery.

In order to answer the question "Why did my anxiety-related problems develop and continue to be a problem?" you need to know about conditioned responses, a phenomenon I call "time tunneling," and how emotions are generated. The material in this chapter and the next covers these three topics and it is the same information I covered with Mary, Robert, Kimberly, and hundreds of others as their first step on the road to recovery. Understanding these three factors helps you develop a more accurate understanding of why your symptoms developed and form the foundation of many of the skills needed to return to a normal life.

Conditioned Responses

At the turn of the century, a Russian scientist named I.P. Pavlov conducted what is now considered a classic experiment. He presented a neutral stimulus, such as ringing a bell, to hungry dogs. He then gave the dogs food which caused them to salivate. With repetition, the neutral stimulus (the bell) became associated with the food and would, by itself, cause salivation. This type of conditioning is called a conditioned response.

Before Conditioning: Bell + Food   ⟶   Salivate

After Conditioning: Bell   ⟶   Salivate

Many human reactions and behaviors are a type of conditioned response. Consider the saying "Mom's cooking tastes best." Mom could be a terrible cook and the saying would still be true because her children would have been conditioned to the taste of her cooking. This explains why food in foreign countries often tastes "funny." The same is true with fashions in clothing. Pictures of clothes worn ten years ago look odd because we have been slowly reconditioning ourselves to the styles of today. In addition, many daily activities such as driving a car or doing simple chores around the house have a host of conditioned responses associated with them. Indeed, it would be difficult if not impossible to function in daily life without these automatic responses.

Posttraumatic Stress Disorder

While conditioned responses play an important role in all forms of anxiety-related problems, they are easiest to understand in posttraumatic stress disorder. Posttraumatic stress disorder is the term used to describe the symptoms that a person experiences after a severe trauma. During World War I, posttraumatic stress disorder was referred to as shell shock; during World War II it was called battle fatigue. Today, the posttraumatic stress disorder model is applied to any situation where a normal person goes through an abnormal and traumatic experience such as rape, assault, physical trauma, major surgery, a natural disaster, or wartime combat duty. It can even be triggered by simply witnessing a traumatic event such as a horrible accident.

While there are many symptoms that people with posttraumatic stress disorder can experience, some of the more common ones include:

- Recurring images of the traumatic event.
- A feeling that the traumatic event is occurring in the present.
- Recurring distressing dreams of the trauma.
- Intense physical discomfort when exposed to events that symbolize or resemble some aspect of the traumatic event.

In addition to the above, they often avoid places or things associated with the trauma, or experience a general numbing that can range from avoidance of thoughts or feelings associated with the trauma to a general feeling of detachment or estrangement from others. There are also usually two or more forms of body arousal present that can range from irritability and difficulty falling asleep or staying asleep to outbursts of anger and an exaggerated startled response.

Kimberly presents a vivid example of posttraumatic stress disorder. After her assault, driving by the school or thinking about returning to work would frequently trigger what are often called "flashbacks," episodes, where Kimberly would re-experience the assault in various ways. Sometimes, the incident would replay in her mind in such a clear and vivid manner that she felt as if the assault were actually occurring again. Other times, she became anxious when an adolescent similar in appearance to the person who assaulted her passed by in a store or on the street.

These types of responses are basically a type of conditioned response. When you think you are in danger, whatever sensory stimulation occurring at that time —sights, sounds, odors, tactile sensations— become associated with danger and trigger what is commonly called the "fight or flight" response in your body whenever you encounter that stimulus in the future. It makes no difference whether the danger is real or imaginary. The more intensely you perceive the danger, the stronger the effect. This response has been very important for human survival, especially when we lived in more primitive conditions. If a certain sight, sound, smell, or touch meant danger, people had to respond immediately in order to survive. This response still helps people respond quickly to danger whether they are in a war zone or simply driving to work.

One of the things that make this type of conditioned responses seem so mysterious is that there is no conscious thought associated with them. They are automatic, unconscious reactions. A simple way to understand this is to pretend that you are connected to a device that can give you an electric shock. I then administer a shock every time I say the word "purple". If I continue to do this, you will begin to twitch whenever I say, "Purple." Then, even though I disconnect the wires, destroy the device, and explain that you will not be shocked any more, I can still say the "purple" and you will twitch.

Sights, Sounds and
Other Sensations Occuring + Danger ⟶ Fight-or-Flight Response
When Danger Was Percieved

Sights, Sounds and
Other Sensations Occuring ⟶ Fight-or-Flight Response
When Danger Was Percieved

This is an important point because many believe that once they understand the causes of a problem, the problem will disappear. Unfortunately, while insight is useful, insight alone usually does not change the way a person thinks and acts. This is especially true for conditioned responses. This does not mean that insight is worthless. Insight and knowledge have an important role to play in quieting conditioned responses. To see why, let's return to the electric shock example.

If, you believe me when I say that you will no longer be shocked and I continue to say "purple" over and over without giving you a shock, you will stop twitching after some time has passed. You will become desensitized to the word. Indeed, this is what happened in Kimberly's case. Over time, she again became comfortable in the various situations that had been triggering symptoms when she first came to see me. This is the second point about condition responses. It is possible to desensitize yourself so that a stimulus or "trigger" will no longer set off a conditioned response.

Why then, do the conditioned responses associated with anxiety-related problems continue to persist and often become even more intense? The answer is that they are reinforced by the way a person thinks about and reacts to them. If you don't believe me when I say that I will no longer shock you, you might begin to worry about when the next shock will come, and tell yourself negative things about what will happen when I shock you again. This will reinforce the conditioned response to the word purple.

If you believe that there should be no reaction to the word purple as soon as you know that there will be no more shocks, you might become alarmed and begin to think that there is something wrong because you are still reacting to the word purple. Both of these can reinforce the startle response associated with the word, "purple" and keep the conditioned response active. This makes having a clear understanding of why your symptoms developed and learning to tell yourself the truth about what causes and maintains your anxiety an important part of the desensitization process.

We will return to this in more detail in later chapters. But for now, we need to deepen your understanding of the forces that cause anxiety-related problems to develop and look at another source of conditioned responses.

The Time Tunnel

When people respond to the present as if they were in the past, I refer to them as being in the "time tunnel." Time tunneling is a type of conditioned response that helps explain why people who were raised in troubled homes often find themselves trapped in dysfunctional patterns. Robert is a good example. The responses he developed to the physical and verbal abuse from his father, the verbal abuse from his mother, and the threat of being beaten up in school became so deeply embedded as a conditioned response that it followed him into his adult life. Whenever he was around anyone who "felt" like his parents or one of the bullies at school, he reacted as he had when he was young. He would become anxious and non-assertive.

This conditioned response became particularly troublesome at work. Whenever Robert had a meeting with his supervisor, who happened to be abrasive and sometimes unreasonable, he would not speak up or confront the supervisor. This caused him to agree to things he later regretted. When Robert left meetings with his supervisor, he was often filled with feelings of disgust and self-loathing. What was happening was simple. Whenever he was around his supervisor, the strong conditioning that took place when he was a boy was triggered by the supervisor, who "felt" like Robert's father and the bullies at school. Because these people were dangerous, Robert had learned to keep quiet and avoid conflict with them. As an adult, Robert, without know it, was confusing the past with the present. He was caught in the time tunnel every time he met with his supervisor.

Escaping the Time Tunnel

While learning the principles for escaping from the time tunnel is simple, it usually takes time and effort to old patterns and replace them with new ones.

The first step in escaping the time tunnel is to identify specific feelings, thoughts, or behaviors that indicate you are experiencing the present as if it were the past and triggering old behaviors. This usually involves anxiety or anger for which there is no reasonable reason along with actions that tend to be self-defeating and which are not a reasonable response to the situation. Once you have identified these triggers, you will start to become more and more aware of your response when it occurs.

The second step is to reorient yourself to the present whenever you see yourself repeating a pattern from the past. A simple way to do this is to:

- State what is happening
- State what is real

Robert began to use this approach by identifying meetings with his supervisor as situations that often drew him into the time tunnel. Once he realized that he was reacting to his supervisor as if he were still a little boy in the presence of his angry father or school tormentors, he began using this approach to keep himself in the present. Here is an example of the type of self-talk Robert would say to himself just before going into a meeting with his supervisor:

What's Happening:
> I'm starting to go through the time tunnel. The feelings I'm experiencing are responses from the past. They were appropriate when I was little. Now it's time to come back to the present.

What's Real:

> My supervisor is not my father. He is just my supervisor. I am not a helpless little boy trapped at home or school anymore. I'm an adult with adult skills and abilities. I'm not going to get beaten up. I'm just going to have a routine discussion of job assignments in my unit.

At first, Robert had to repeat these statements several times to himself prior to a meeting with his supervisor, and sometimes during the meeting. As he did this, he found it easier and easier to react to his supervisor in a more adult manner. As Robert became more skilled at staying in the present with his supervisor, he began to notice when he became anxious and fidgety around certain other people when there was no reason to be anxious. He identified these people as being similar to one of his tormentors from the past in some way. Sometimes it was the person's voice. Other times it was the person's appearance or posture.

Robert also realized that situations where he was criticized often triggered childhood patterns he had developed in response to his critical mother. In his first marriage, he became very angry whenever his wife criticized him. Even simple comments triggered explosive anger. This eventually caused his first wife to leave him. In his second marriage he controlled his anger by swallowing it and remaining calm on the outside. This eventually turned out to be one of the factors behind his gagging problem; he was gagging on the words he was swallowing both at home and at work.

Four Common Traits in Adults with Abusive Childhoods

There are four common traits found in adults who have been abused as children. A person who has experienced severe sexual, physical, or emotional abuse will usually have all four. A person who experienced less severe abuse may only experience some of the traits. Sometimes, a particular trait may only interfere with a person's life in a limited number of situations where the person is time-tunneling.

Tendency to Be Triggered by Specific Events

The first trait is the tendency to be triggered by specific events, which has been called time tunneling in this chapter. Mary, Robert, and Kimberly each experienced anxiety that was triggered by situations and events that resembled childhood experiences. Because Kimberly's background was much less abusive than Mary's or Robert's, she had the least amount of difficulty in this area.

Difficulty Modulating Emotions

The second trait is difficulty modulating emotions. This means that a person frequently becomes overly anxious or angry, and, once angered or frightened, finds it difficult to calm down. This is especially true when events trigger time tunneling where the exaggerated danger and helplessness a person experienced as a child is being triggered by something in the present. To make matters worse, the strong emotions being triggered reduce a person's ability to reason making it even more difficult to manage them.

An adult who had to suppress emotions as a child may also find it difficult to feel emotions at a low level because the tendency to suppress emotions has become automatic. In this person, emotions are only felt when they are very strong. Thus, this person either experiences too much of an emotion or nothing at all. Robert, for example, would talk about an emotionally intense issue in a flat and emotionless manner.

Tendency to View Oneself and the World Negatively

The third trait is a tendency to view oneself and the world negatively. The three most common areas affected are the ability to trust, feel safe, and believe that it is possible to bring about desired outcomes. Two additional areas in terms of one's self-image are whether or not one is normal and whether or not one is lovable. This is discussed in detail in the next chapter.

The nature of the abuse can greatly affect the form of these negative views. For instance, if a person was abused by a stranger, he or she may have a sense of safety when close to loved ones, and a sense of danger when far away from them. However, if a person was abused by someone who was supposed to protect and give love, the identification of what and who are "safe" becomes confused.

Reduced Ability to Understand Painful Events

The fourth trait is a reduced ability to understand painful events. People with this tendency find that they often go into a daze or become confused, especially when they are stressed, dealing with conflict, or emotionally upset. When a child is being abused and cannot escape physically, the child often takes the only other form of escape possible: dissociation. Dissociation is the ability to remove oneself mentally from a situation. The more frequent and severe the abuse, the greater the tendency to remove oneself mentally from the painful experience. Unfortunately, this automatic habit pattern often continues into adulthood. This causes the person to dissociate whenever a current event triggers pain from the past.

These tendencies can create many different types of problems. For example, people with abusive childhoods often find it difficult to distinguish unhealthy individuals from healthy ones. Their childhood experiences taught them to ignore the important indicators that are signs of danger to those raised in healthy families. Instead, they "numb out" or use an old response pattern that causes them to walk into harm's way without even knowing it.

These tendencies can greatly affect a person's spiritual side. It's difficult to find satisfying answers to questions such as "Is there a God?" "Is there a larger meaning to life?" and "Is it worth giving a part of myself to others?" In addition, abused children often develop a self-concept that contains beliefs about being dirty, inadequate, guilty, or responsible for what happened. As a result, they often make up a "cover story" and try to hide who they really are. All of this makes it difficult for them to develop healthy relationships and function effectively.

Summary of Key Ideas

1. Conditioned responses are automatic, unconscious reactions that play a major role in human behavior.
2. Conditioned responses play a major role in all anxiety-related problems. This is easiest to see in posttraumatic stress disorder.
3. While insight is useful, insight alone usually does not change unconscious conditioned responses.
4. It takes time to desensitize yourself to the triggers associated with conditioned responses.
5. Time tunneling refers to times when a person responds to the present as if it were the past.
6. To escape time tunneling and return to the present, state what is happening, then state what is real.
7. Adults who have been abused as children often have one or more of the following traits: (1) a tendency to be triggered by specific events, (2) difficulty modulating emotions, (3) a tendency to view themselves and the world negatively, and (4) a reduced ability to understand painful events.

Recommended Activities

Identify Triggers That Cause You to Time Tunnel

This chapter describes the source of problem behaviors that tend to be the most difficult to change: the automatic patterns you learned while growing up. While they are not the only factors, they do play a major role in most anxiety-related problems. Be sure to work through, systematically, the recommended activities that follow.

Review the genogram, the descriptions of the adults who raised you, and the early recollections you completed at the end of chapter 2. Identify as many childhood patterns as you can that you still repeat today. Keep in mind that the solutions of childhood are often the problems of adulthood. Whenever you notice yourself reacting to the present as if it were the past, use the simple approach of stating what's happening and what's real to reorient yourself to the present. It's also useful to use this approach when you are about to enter a situation that often causes you to time tunnel so you can stay in the present.

If there is a situation where time-tunneling is especially strong, write out a "what's happening; what's real" statement and take time to memorize it. Since strong emotions interfere with your ability to think clearly, having a memorized statement will help to calm you down when you are in a situation that triggers time-tunneling. You may even want to write your statement on a card or make a note of it in your phone so you can take it with you.

Begin Keeping a Journaling

Begin keeping a journal. Use your journal to complete the written activities, list problems and concerns, record insights, and keep track of your progress. As the chapters unfold, you will find that your journal is an extremely effective tool for growth. You don't need to use anything expensive or fancy. A simple spiral-bound notebook is fine. Some people prefer keeping their journal on a computer or tablet. A few like the feel of a more expensive bound book with blank pages. You decide which is most comfortable for you.

As you work with your journal, keep in mind that privacy is essential. This makes it easier to write honestly and openly. Do not write for an "unseen audience"; the need to please these invisible watchers will cause you to lose much of the benefit of keeping a journal.

The main value of a journal is not the permanent record you create but the work required to create it. After several months you may decide to destroy your journal or keep it as a source of encouragement for the progress it records.

A Word about Sleep

When you are not sleeping well, your body becomes more reactive and your ability to think clearly is reduced. Chronic sleep problems can cause your symptoms to escalate and interfere with your ability to learn the skills described in this book. In fact, those with poor sleep habits often find that simply improving the quality of their sleep significantly reduces their symptoms.

Since chronic sleep problems can be caused by many different medications and physical problems, it's always best to discuss sleep problems with your physician. If they are a major issue, you may even want to consult a physician who specializes in sleep disturbances.

Fortunately, many sleep problems are simply due to poor sleep habits or excessive worry that interferes with sleep. Here are several suggestions for developing what is commonly called good sleep hygiene:

- Establish a regular time to go to bed and get up. Avoid making up for lost sleep on weekends or holidays. If you have been going to bed and getting up at widely varying times, you may need to reset your biological clock by following a regular schedule for sleep. It's alright to take naps if they are taken on a fixed schedule and you make appropriate adjustments to your nighttime schedule.

- Reserve your bed for sleeping and sex. Watching television, reading, or doing other activities in bed is one of the most common reasons for difficulty in falling asleep. If you are finding it very difficult to sleep well, make the bedroom off-limits to everything except sleep and sex.

- Create a proper environment for sleep. People often forget about obvious things such as making sure the bedroom is dark, quiet, and well ventilated.

- Develop a routine that prepares you for sleep. This routine becomes a conditioned response trigger that tells your body, "It's time to fall asleep." A typical routine might include brushing your hair and teeth, pulling down the sheets, and setting out clothes for the next day.

- For two hours prior to sleeping, restrict your activities to those that are relaxing. These activities might include taking a hot bath or shower, reading, watching television, praying, or meditating. Avoid anxiety-provoking activities like paying bills or arguing.

- Use one of the relaxation response techniques described in appendix 4.

- If you've been lying awake for twenty minutes, get up and go to a different part of the house. This also applies if you have spent twenty minutes using one of the relaxation response exercises in appendix 4 and are still awake. Get up.

- Do a relaxing activity such as reading a book or watching television until you feel tired. At first, you may find yourself spending much of the night out of bed, and get only four or five hours of sleep altogether, but these short periods of continuous, sound sleep will gradually expand to fill the night. Do not nap for more than thirty minutes during the day while you're reestablishing a normal sleep pattern.

- Avoid caffeine, nicotine, heavy meals, and strenuous exercise for three to five hours before bedtime.

- Exercise during the day. Exercising in the late afternoon increases the amount of deep sleep you get in the first half of the night. Even a brisk walk around the block may help. However, exercise just before sleeping interferes with sleep. It takes a few hours after exercising for your body to be ready for sleep.

- Create "noise screens." If noise in your surroundings makes it difficult for you to go to sleep or wakes you up, block out the noise with a sound screen. There are a wide variety of sound screens available that produce relaxing background sounds. When traveling, a simple sound screen can be created by placing a radio next to your bed and tuning it between stations to produce white noise that masks the sounds around you. Some find that ear-plugs or a combination of ear-plugs and a sound screen helps.

- Stay away from alcohol. Even moderate amounts of alcohol can disturb sleep or create a backlash of sleeplessness later in the night that makes sleep problems worse.

- Avoid using sleeping medications regularly. Over-the-counter remedies (usually antihistamines) are often not a very effective long-term solution. One exception seems to be melatonin that can be purchased in tablet form in health food stores. While melatonin can be helpful, be sure to consult your physician before using it. Prescription drugs can alter normal sleep patterns and suppress deep sleep or REM (rapid eye movement) sleep—the time during sleep when you are dreaming. They can also leave you groggy the next day. Because the body becomes tolerant of some drugs, higher and higher doses are needed, leading to dependency. In fact, sleeping pills are often one of the main causes of long-term sleeplessness.

- If you get drowsy during the day, change the pace of your activity. The most "natural" way to keep awake is to move: Get up from your chair, pace the floor, and stretch. Try light rests and creative breaks instead of alcohol, cigarettes, or coffee.

- If worrying about problems makes it difficult for you to fall asleep or keeps you awake in the middle of the night, try the following:
    - Get out of bed and go to another part of the house. Develop a concrete plan for dealing with the problem and write it down on a piece of paper. After you've developed your plan, write a one- or two-sentence summary of what you are going to do.
    - If you are drowsy when you complete your plan, go on to the next step. If you are not drowsy, do a relaxing activity to wind down.
    - Go to bed and use one of the relaxation response techniques described in appendix 4.
    - If you find yourself thinking about the problem, recite the one- or two-sentence summary you wrote and use a relaxation-response exercise to distract yourself.
    - If worry over problems prior to going to sleep is a recurring pattern, establish a regular time at least two hours before to your bedtime during which you think about your problems and develop concrete plans for dealing with them.

- Some people are awakened by panic attacks in the middle of the night. Often, there is no memory of having been dreaming. Current research suggests that nocturnal panic attacks where there is no recollection of a dream are due to some neurological mechanism that is not understood at present. If you experience nocturnal panic attacks but are able to return to sleep fairly easily, continue to do whatever you do to return to sleep. However, if nocturnal panic attacks are triggering negative self-talk and high levels of anxiety that make it difficult for you to return to sleep, do the following:

- Prepare an index card with coping statements such as "My nocturnal panic attacks are due to a neurological quirk. They are not dangerous. The feelings they generate are uncomfortable but they last only a little while. Find something relaxing to do until you feel drowsy. Then, go back to bed and use your relaxation-response exercise." After you've made your index card, place it beside your bed or in your bathroom.

- When you experience a nocturnal panic attack, get up and wash your face so you become fully awake. Once you're fully awake, read the card you've prepared.

- Next, spend about five to twenty minutes with a distracting and relaxing activity that allows your body to settle down, such as reading a book, watching television or having a cup of warm milk (avoid cocoa since it has caffeine in it).

- Finally, when you begin to feel drowsy, go back to bed. If you are still a little restless, use one of the relaxation-response techniques in appendix 4 to help you get back to sleep.

A Word for People with Severe Anxiety

If your anxiety is severe and seriously interfering with your life, seek professional help. Methodologies such as Eye Movement Desensitization and Reprocessing (EMDR) can be very useful. However, they do require you to work with a trained therapist. Appendix 1 discusses this and other forms of help in more detail.

CHAPTER 4

The Mystery of Emotions

In order to understand how anxiety can change from a mild everyday occurrence that everyone experiences into an uncontrollable nightmare, you need a general understanding of emotions. This will then allow you to gain a full understanding of the dynamics that lead to anxiety-related problems and serve as the foundation for long-term recovery.

Emotions can be very mysterious. They often come and go with no apparent reason and can make life wonderful or miserable. The importance of emotions to our experience is seen by the fact that throughout the ages in all cultures, emotional conflict is a key component of stories, music, and theater. You can also find scores of books dealing with the various aspects of emotions filling the self-help section of bookstores. Yet, most people have little understanding of how emotions work and why we have them. In view of this, let's begin by answering two basic questions: "What are emotions?" and "What is their function?"

What Are Emotions?

Emotions are a complex process with subjective, physical, and mental components. One part of the subjective aspect of emotions is the "feelings" you experience with different emotions. When something is objective, anyone can observe and experience it.

However, the way you feel when experiencing various emotions is subjective. Only you know what you are feeling. There is no way for you to know if your experience is a similar to or different from what someone else experiences.

A second part of the subjective aspect of emotions is an urge to take action. The stronger the emotion, the stronger the urge to take action you experience. Thus, when you are irritated about something, you might choose to say or do nothing in a given situation. However, as you become angry, your emotion generates a stronger and stronger desire to say or do something.

The physical part of emotions refer to how they prepare the body for action through what is commonly known as the fight-or-flight response. This response quiets activities such as digestion that might interfere with intense activity and increases activities such as your breathing and heartrate that are needed for intense activity.

Another physical aspect of emotions is the nonverbal role they play in communication by causing subtle changes in your facial expression, body posture, and tone of voice. A simple exercise illustrates this point. Say the phrase "I love you" as if you were speaking to your lover. Now say it as if you are asking a question. Finally, in a lighthearted manner as if you were speaking in a casual manner to an acquaintance. Each evokes subtle changes in your facial expression, posture, and tone of voice that make the meaning clear to the other person without any further explanation. The changes that take place in you as your emotions change and the ability of other people to recognize them are thought to be hard wired into us from birth, making emotions a powerful form of communication.

The mental aspect of emotions refers the fact that emotions are usually triggered by your interpretation of an event. This interpretation can be conscious or unconscious as with conditioned responses.

Putting this all together, we can diagram the subjective, physical and mental processes that generate emotions as follows:

Event $\longrightarrow$ Interpretation $\longrightarrow$ Emotion $\longrightarrow$ Action

As events occur around you, you make conscious and unconscious interpretations about what they mean. These interpretations trigger the various emotions you experience. Your emotions then cause you to take action in response to the events. Sometimes, the action you take in response to an emotion is mental, such as when you disagree with someone but decide not to say or do anything. Other times, it involves both thought and physical action, such as telling someone what you want or getting something you need.

This model is called a cognitive model of emotions (cognitive refers to thinking) because it stresses the mental factors that generate emotions. While the majority of your emotions are generated through the process diagramed above, there are some important exceptions. Many diseases, chemicals, injuries, and genetic defects can trigger emotional responses. A few examples would be mood-altering drugs that can produce a wide range of inappropriate emotions, thyroid problems that cause anxiety, head trauma that causes emotional outbursts and genetic defects that cause Bipolar disorder or endogenous depression. There also seem to be some emotional responses that are "hard wired" into us such as the panic that grips us when we can't breathe.

In addition to the above non-cognitive sources of emotional responses, several common everyday physical factors such as hunger, fatigue, illness, or stress can reduce your ability to think clearly and cause you to misinterpret events. This misinterpretation can then trigger exaggerated or inappropriate emotions. A simple example is how we sometimes overreact to simple situations when sick, hungry, ill, or under stress.

Why Do We Have Emotions?

The key word to remember when answering the question "Why do we have emotions?" is "needs." Emotions are generated in direct response to whether we perceive that: a need has been met, a threat is present, or a loss has occurred.

In simple terms, it works like this: A part of your mind constantly evaluates the events unfolding around you in relation to your needs and wants. This process of assigning meaning to events is usually done automatically and unconsciously. If a need or want has been satisfied or will soon be satisfied, you experience the various positive emotions such as joy, excitement, or satisfaction. If a threat is present, you experience anger or fear, and if you perceive a loss, you experience sadness. Keep in mind that I'm using the words anger, fear, and sadness in a very broad sense. Anger can range from irritation to rage, fear from apprehension to panic, and sadness from disappointment to deep depression.

This process of interpreting needs and wants can be diagramed as follows:

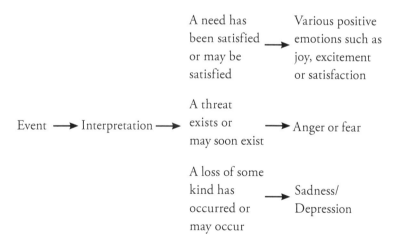

Because events are often complex, they can satisfy some needs and frustrate others. This is why you often experience conflicting emotions. For example, your child is leaving for college or to start a new job in another city and you feel both happy and sad at the same time.

Putting all of the above together, we can diagram the different components for each step in the interpretation process as follows:

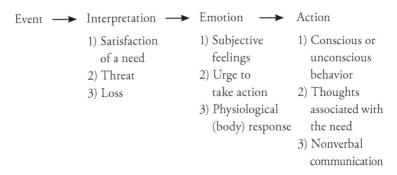

Event ⟶ Interpretation ⟶ Emotion ⟶ Action

	Interpretation	Emotion	Action
	1) Satisfaction of a need	1) Subjective feelings	1) Conscious or unconscious behavior
	2) Threat	2) Urge to take action	2) Thoughts associated with the need
	3) Loss	3) Physiological (body) response	3) Nonverbal communication

Kimberly presents a good example of how all of these components work together. She longed for a permanent relationship and periodically would meet someone she found attractive. As with most complex situations, there were many different interpretations occurring at the same time. There was the potential for satisfying a need along with the threat that she might be rejected. This, in turn, heightened the loss she felt because she was single. The emotions generated by these elements were a mixture of excitement, anxiety, and melancholy. The mental actions generated by these emotions were thoughts of hope and pleasurable fantasies as well as thoughts of dread and visions of being alone for the rest of her life. The physical actions taken included arranging times she could spend with this person, as well as some avoidance in the form of acting shy and awkward. The physical responses that were part of her nonverbal communication included changes in the eyes, face, and body that are typical of a person who is deeply infatuated with someone.

Human Needs

Since emotions are generated in response to our needs, it is useful to take a look at the various needs that you have. Unfortunately, the way human needs are categorized is still a much debated topic among researchers. For our purposes, the simplest way to look at them is to group them into the following four categories:

Physical Needs

This group of needs includes all of the physical things you need to feel safe such as food, shelter, and freedom from harm.

Mental Needs

This is a rather broad range of needs relating to your need to understand the world and how it works. To keep things simple, I'll include the need to explore and learn, and the need to create in this category. These drive your desire to understand your circumstances and how you can accomplish the tasks you wish to complete.

Relationship Needs

Relationship needs can be summarized as your need to have a deep emotional connection to something. In healthy individuals this is usually seen as the desire to have a positive relationship with another person or group of people such one's family as well as pets.

Spiritual Needs

This group has to do with your need to find meaning in life and death. Your spiritual needs cause you to seek answers to questions such as "Why am I here?" "What happens when I die?" "Does God exist?"

Those who believe that life has a spiritual dimension beyond the purely physical and mental realities of science find their answers to these types of questions in the religious realm. People who do not believe in a soul or spiritual dimension usually seek answers to these questions through philosophy and reason. If you belong to this group and do not like the term spiritual, you can think of these needs as existential needs since they deal with the problem of finding meaning for your existence.

The above four categories can be diagramed as follows.

Physical
(need for safety)

Mental
(need to understand the world
and how it works

Relationship
(need to connect with others)

Spiritual/Existential
(need to find meaning in life and death)

In the above list, the lower needs are usually more important to a person than the higher ones. For example, if you have a well-founded belief about who you are, your place in the world, and your purpose in life (mental and spiritual needs) and healthy supportive relationships (relationship needs), it is easier to feel secure even when you are lacking physical necessities or suffering illness (physical needs). At the same time, if you have no sense of purpose and poor relationships (relationship and spiritual needs), you can have an abundance of things and success at work (physical and mental needs) and be miserable except when sedated by temporary thrills.

Core Beliefs

You have many beliefs about yourself, others and the world around you. These include simple practical beliefs about everyday things such as "water will come out of the shower when I turn it on," along with what I call core beliefs. Core beliefs are the basic assumptions you make about yourself and the world that your mind uses as the basis for the various interpretations you make concerning everyday events. Core beliefs can be divided into beliefs about yourself, relationships, and the world around you. Here are examples of a positive and negative core belief in each of these areas:

Beliefs about yourself:
"I have value" vs. "I am worthless."

Beliefs about relationships:
"Relationships are important and can be very satisfying" vs "Relationships are painful."

Beliefs about the world:
"The world holds many opportunities" vs. "I can't win at anything."

In addition to the conscious beliefs you hold in each of the above areas, there are many conditioned responses acquired over the course of your life that correspond to each area. Because your interpretation of events is mostly, if not completely, unconscious, you are usually unaware of how these conscious beliefs and unconscious conditioned responses interact.

For many, these unconscious conditioned responses will, for the most part, correspond to what they would list as their core beliefs. For example Mary would say that she is not very smart even though I found her to be a bright and insightful woman. However, because she had been told repeatedly during childhood that she was stupid, she came to believe it and her behavior reflected the core belief, "I'm not as smart as most."

While Mary's unconscious conditioned responses reflected her conscious beliefs, Robert, like many others had areas of his life where he said one thing but behaved in a way that was contrary to what he said. Whenever this is the case, one's behavior is usually being driven by unconscious conditioned responses rather than by one's conflicting conscious beliefs.

Because, as a child, Robert was physically, emotionally, and verbally abused both at home and at school, his experience was that conflict was dangerous and often caused him physical or emotional pain. The danger and fear associated with his parents and the older children who had bullied him produced a conditioned response that became associated with all authority figures.

Because Robert viewed himself as a competent and strong adult, he was genuinely puzzled by the way he became non-assertive when dealing with his supervisor. Because he acted as if conflict was dangerous, we identified this as one of the core beliefs that was driving his behavior even though it was mainly an unconscious conditioned response.

Labeling these types of conditioned responses as core beliefs and describing them with descriptive phrases such as "conflict is dangerous" or "relationships are painful" provides you with a powerful tool for quieting these types of responses. Much more will be said about this in the next chapter. However, before moving on, take some time to identify the core beliefs your mind is using to interpret events.

Summary of Key Ideas

1. Emotions are a complex process with subjective, physical, and mental components.

2. The cognitive model of emotions sees emotions as being the result of your interpretation of events. This interpretation is often an unconscious process.

3. While the cognitive model explains how most everyday emotions are generated, there are important exceptions where emotions are generated through non-cognitive means.

4. The function of emotions is to generate thoughts and actions that satisfy needs and protect you from threat and loss.

5. Satisfying a need generates positive emotions. Perceived or real threats generate anxiety or anger. Perceived or real losses generate sadness.

6. One way to view human needs is to divide them into four categories: physical, mental, relationship, and spiritual.

7. Core beliefs are the basic assumptions you make about yourself and the world that your mind uses as the basis for the various interpretations you make concerning everyday events.

8. Core beliefs are a combination of stated beliefs and conditioned responses. You're your stated beliefs are in conflict with a conditioned response, you sometimes respond to a situation in a way that you don't understand.

9. Labeling these types of problematic responses as core beliefs stated as simple sentences such as "conflict is dangerous" gives you a tool you can use to reduce their influence over you.

Recommended Activities

Activity Overview: Lay a Strong Foundation

The information and activities in this chapter form a foundation for the chapters that follow. Take your time with it, and be sure to reread it before going on to the next chapter. You may be surprised at what you missed in your first reading. If you find it difficult to understand, read it a third time.

Identify Basic Concepts You Learned in Childhood

One of the key concepts in this chapter is the idea that emotions are triggered by an interpretation of events in terms of whether they meet or frustrate a need, a threat is present or a loss has occurred. Furthermore, this interpretation is based on both conscious beliefs and unconscious associations.

As you go through this exercise, keep in mind that it focuses on beliefs and associations that cause problems. In addition to negative beliefs and associations, Mary, Robert, and Kimberly also brought many positive beliefs out of childhood. For example, Mary's success in running and school helped her develop the core belief, "I can succeed if I work hard." Kimberly's close relationship with her mother and stepfather gave her the core belief, "I'm loved and lovable." One of Robert's positive core beliefs was, "I'm good with my hands." This was reflected in his skill with tools and working with mechanical things. When working with problem areas in your life, it's easy to forget that, in addition to negative core beliefs, you developed many positive core beliefs.

Keeping this in mind, here are some examples of negative beliefs and associations Mary, Robert, and Kimberly brought into their adult lives. Some, such as Mary's belief "I can't do anything right," are beliefs that were consciously held core beliefs and matched their behavior. Others, such as Robert's core belief that "conflict is dangerous," were unconscious conditioned responses that conflicted with their stated beliefs.

Mary

> I can't do anything right. I'm inferior to others. I'm not
>   as intelligent or capable as they are.
> When problems arise, don't look, don't feel, run away.
> Love hurts, protect yourself.
> The world is dangerous. I'm not safe.

Robert

> Conflict is dangerous.
> People in authority are dangerous.
> Something is wrong with me. I'm inferior to others.
> There's nothing I can do to make a difference.
> People always let you down.
> Numb yourself, don't feel anything.

Kimberly

> Winning is what counts.
> I have to be the best in order to have value.
> Mistakes are not acceptable.
> I must be strong and never show weakness.

The above are just partial lists of the problem beliefs and associations that were identified in these three individuals. However, they clearly show that Mary and Robert were very limited in their ability to form intimate relationships and deal with problems effectively. As you will see in the next few chapters, this played a major role in the development of their symptoms. Even Kimberly, who had a tremendous number of strengths from childhood, had one major weakness: the needed to avoid making mistakes and always to be the best at whatever she did. While it's good to want to do well, Kimberly carried this desire to an extreme, where any mistake was a major defeat. This became a chief obstacle for her as she wrestled with recovering from the aftereffects of her assault.

While it is not too difficult to list your conscious negative beliefs about yourself, others, and the world, identifying negative unconscious core beliefs is more difficult. Because they are the result of unconscious conditioned responses, you've probably never thought much about them. Fortunately, you can uncover them using a simple method based on the old adage "If it looks like a duck, talks like a duck, and walks like a duck, it's probably a duck." Rephrasing this saying, it becomes: "If you act like you believe something, speak like you believe something, and think like you believe something, you believe it." This belief is one of the core beliefs you are trying to identify.

In order to apply this principle to yourself, you need to have completed the exercises in chapter 2. If you have not completed them, stop and do so before you continue with this one. If you have completed the descriptions of your family and early childhood experiences, review them and make a list of those negative beliefs and behaviors that have caused you problems in life. The easiest way to do this is to review your genogram and the descriptions of your early childhood then ask yourself, "What kinds of core beliefs would a child growing up in this situation develop?" Keep in mind the idea that "if you act, speak, or think like you believe something," that core belief is probably playing an important role in your behavior whether you consciously agree with it or not. Here is a small sampling of the many different types of negative core beliefs that underlie dysfunctional behaviors. As you read through them identify any that describe some aspect of your behavior, thoughts or the emotions you experience.

Examples of Negative Beliefs and Associations about Yourself

I'm inferior to others (other ways of expressing this idea are: There is something wrong with me, I don't measure up, or I'm not as intelligent or capable as others).

I'm worthless.

I have no power. There's nothing I can do to make a difference in how events turn out.

I'm not lovable.

I'm dirty.

I'm ugly.

I'm a bad person.

I cannot succeed.

I'm incompetent.

I'm crazy.

Examples of Negative Core Beliefs and Associations about Relationships

Intimacy is dangerous (or painful), therefore, don't get close.

Conflict is dangerous.

People in authority are dangerous.

You can't trust anyone.

Sooner or later, people always abandon you.

The opposite sex is inferior/superior.

I'm responsible for how others feel.

If people see how I don't measure up, they will not like me.

Never discuss weaknesses, death, or illness with others. They might be hurt or think badly of you and leave you.

Examples of Negative Core Beliefs and Associations about the World

> The world is fearful and dangerous.
> There is no safe place in the world.
> When bad things happen to me, it's my fault.
> I have no power or control.
> Life is meaningless.
> To live is to suffer.
> Keep a close watch on your body because it is weak and fragile and something terrible can go wrong at any time.

If you find it difficult to identify your core beliefs and associations, you might find it useful to discuss this with someone you trust and who knows you well. Others often can see us more clearly than we can. If you don't have someone like this in your life, you might find it helpful to work with a trained therapist.

CHAPTER 5

Developing Your
Explanation for "Why"

In this chapter we'll explore the dynamics that generate panic disorder. Let's start by looking at the development of Mary's symptoms. As with many, her panic disorder developed in stages. Mary flew frequently for her work and on one flight she experienced anxiety due to an unusually strong turbulence. While approaching her destination, the airplane hit a downdraft and dropped several hundred feet triggering a sense of panic. As she prepared to board the plane for her next trip, she experienced anxiety that seemed to come for no reason. While she didn't know it, her anxiety was the result of the frightening experience on her previous flight had generated a conditioned response where flying was now associated with danger. Because Mary was frightened by the sudden anxiety she felt, she began engaging in what is called "negative anticipation" or "what if" thinking. She began to think:

"What if I panic on this flight?"

"What if I get so anxious that I lose control?"

"What will people think?"

"Maybe I have some sort of 'mental problem."

"Maybe I have some sort of physical problem that my doctor missed."

These types of thoughts are a normal and reasonable response when frightening sensations are experienced for which there is no

59

explanation. Having sound, reasonable answers for these types of questions that you understand and agree with helps you to stop this type of thinking. It also helps you to shift your focus to the work that is necessary to achieve long-term recovery.

In addition to her negative anticipation, Mary began to do what is usually called "body scanning" or "internalization". She began to monitor her body and look for signs that might indicate the mysterious and frightening symptoms were returning. As she waited for her flight, body scanning caused her to notice all sorts of sensations and reactions that she had never noticed before. All of these reactions were normal, but because she didn't understand them and had never noticed them before, she incorrectly identified them as signs that the terrible sensations she feared were returning.

As Mary boarded her flight and settled into her seat, her negative anticipation increased and triggered what is commonly known as the fight-or-flight response. This response is designed to decrease all of the reactions in the body that are not necessary for intense activity (such as digestion), and increase all of the reactions that are needed (such as increased heart rate, deeper breathing, sweating, and so on). As Mary noticed the increase in physical symptoms associated with the mysterious anxiety she was feeling, her fear increased. Her increasing fear caused her symptoms to intensify until they became a full blown panic attack. This process is called the anxiety/panic cycle and can be diagramed as follows:

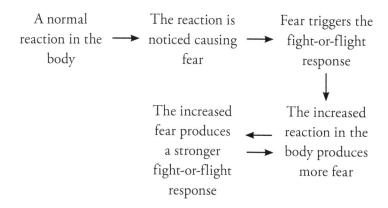

After her flight, Mary now entered the third stage of the process where the fear of anxiety became associated with more and more situations. Because the frightening reactions had occurred a second time without explanation, Mary began to worry and look for possible symptoms in her body in situations other than those associated with flying. For example, one morning during a routine run, she noticed that she was a little dizziness. This was actually a normal out-of-breath sensation that anyone who exercises experiences from time to time. In the past she had never paid much attention to it. Now, because she had become very worried about any unusual sensation, her fear once again caused her to talk herself into a self-generated panic attack. Soon, she was monitoring her body all of the time.

When a person begins monitoring the body as closely as Mary was, they begin to notice all sorts of bodily sensations that were previously unnoticed. Because these sensations seem to be new, the person wrongly assumes that they indicate some sort of disease process or abnormal reaction. In truth, the vast majority of sensations that people report to me are simply normal reactions that were ignored prior to the onset of their anxiety disorder.

For many, the process of worrying and watching their bodies for signs of the dreaded symptoms soon takes on a life of its own. At this point, the conditioned responses discussed in chapter 3 play an important role in the further development of their anxiety. In Mary's case, because she mistakenly associated danger with the normal sensations of running, these sensations became a conditioned-response trigger for anxiety. In fact, with time, just thinking about running would trigger mild anxiety. When Mary noticed this mild anxiety, her negative self-talk would begin the anxiety/panic cycle and sometime increase her anxiety until it became a panic attack.

For Robert, the association of danger with eating became such a strong conditioned response that just thinking of eating would trigger high levels of anxiety for him. Again, it should be pointed out that the initial anxiety generated by this type of conditioned response is completely unconscious. Once danger has been associated with a situation, activity, or bodily sensation, whenever it is experienced, it generates anxiety. A conditioned response like this will become extinguished in time if it is not reinforced with negative self-talk. Unfortunately, most people with anxiety-related problems do not understand this. Whenever they experience this type of conditioned response anxiety, they reinforce it with fearful thoughts, and it becomes stronger.

Over the course of several months, as Mary's anxiety became more pervasive and the panic attacks more frequent, she began avoiding places associated with the terrifying symptoms. As her world grew smaller, her negative anticipation became more exaggerated. She was caught in a vicious circle. It was at this point that we met and she began her journey to recovery.

The Answer Is E

After someone gives me a brief history, I usually ask them, "Why do you think your symptoms first appeared, and why do they continue to be a problem?" Mary, Robert, and Kimberly gave typical responses.

Mary:

> I have panic disorder and low self-esteem and can't seem to manage my life well.

Robert:

> I really don't know why this (his gagging response and anxiety produced by eating) is happening. I think a childhood experience I was told about triggered all of this. My mom told me that when I was two I swallowed a paper clip and they had to hold me upside down and that I almost choked to death. I really never thought much about it but I guess that's what triggered all of this.

Kimberly:

> I know that I have posttraumatic stress disorder because of the assault. But, I don't really know why I can't handle things better. I'm usually a very strong person.

Notice that each of the above explanations is reasonable; they are also not very detailed. In Mary's case, she uses an accurate clinical label, "panic disorder," and a pop psychology term, "low self-esteem." Terms like panic disorder and posttraumatic stress disorder are part of our modern classification system for mental health related problems. They are essential in clinical diagnosis and research. However, while an accurate label often gives the illusion of understanding, it doesn't really help someone understand what caused their condition or why it continues to be a problem. It's like knowing the make and model of a car but having little understanding of how a car works. Unfortunately, the substitution of a label or name for a true understanding of the dynamics of a process or phenomenon is very common.

Using technical labels or popular terms to describe yourself also increases the perception that you are seriously damaged and different from everyone else. One of the tasks that needs to be accomplished in order to achieve long-term recovery is to stop identifying yourself with a disorder and to see yourself as a normal person struggling with a particular problem. You are no different from anyone who has experienced a serious disease or accident and has successfully returned to a normal life. Yours is simply one of the many possible struggles that humans face.

Another error people make is looking for a single cause to explain everything. When I see someone doing this, I often tell them that with human beings, the correct answer is usually "E", which in multiple-choice tests usually means "all of the above." As you will see in the chapters that follow, there was no single cause for Mary, Robert, or Kimberly's struggle with anxiety. Instead, there were several different factors that interacted to trigger their initial symptoms and cause anxiety to continue to be a problem.

The idea that most anxiety-related problems are caused by several factors interacting at the same time is easy to understand. However, because we live in a culture that demands simple answers to complex problems, it often takes time for some to accept it.

Robert's initial explanation —that a childhood trauma caused all of his symptoms— typifies one way that people search for a single cause. While childhood experiences often do play a role in the development and maintenance of anxiety-related problems, they are usually not the primary cause. Another common form of the "one shoe fits all" approach is the idea that anxiety-related problems are due to a "chemical imbalance." The view that biology is the only cause of the problem is very attractive because it offers the hope that the right medication will adjust the imbalance and everything will be fine. While biology, like childhood experiences, often does play an important role, it is usually not the only cause of an anxiety-related problem. In addition, because many people with a variety of the biological factors associated with anxiety disorders have achieved long-term recovery, it is clear that it is the interaction of biology with other non-biological factors that generated their struggle with anxiety. Let's now look at five factors that can combine in various ways to trigger the initial episode of frightening symptoms.

Five Factors That Can Trigger Symptoms

Earlier in this chapter, you learned that Mary's first panic attack occurred when she was traveling and had to fly in an airplane during severe turbulence. On her next flight, it seemed as if a panic attack just "struck out of the blue." Actually, there are five different factors that can interact in various combinations with the beliefs and emotional baggage from childhood to trigger a person's initial panic attack. Let's look at each one individually.

Sensitive Body

Like many people with anxiety-related problems, Mary is sensitive to noise, odors, and a host of things that don't bother the average person. For example, she finds it difficult to go to sleep at her normal bedtime if she has had a cup of coffee late in the afternoon. To

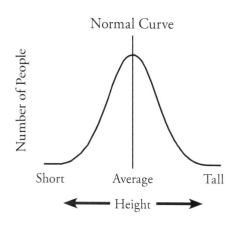

fully understand this sensitivity, consider what you would find if you measured the height of a large number of people. A few would be very tall, a few would be very short, but most would be somewhere near the average height. The bell shaped curve that results from graphing this information is known as a normal curve as shown in the diagram.

If you measured just about any human characteristic —bone thickness, blood chemistry, weight, height etc.— the results would be a normal curve. The sensitivity of the nervous system of people vary in this same way. A person with a sensitive body often has greater 'intuition", and tends to notice more details about others and their environment than less sensitive people. Often, there is also a greater ability to empathize. In fact, this sensitive, empathetic, and intuitive ability is often what others like most about someone with this trait. All of these qualities are simply the result of having a body that is more reactive than the average body and thus able to take in more information than the average person. Unfortunately, a sensitive body also can be easily overloaded. It's like a house where the wiring is not up to code. If you plug too many electrical devices into a particular circuit, it becomes overloaded, and the breaker trips. People with sensitive bodies feel the effects of stress more easily than those who are less reactive.

Another factor that can complicate the picture for women is the actions of their hormones. A lot of the women I've worked with report that their anxiety symptoms are often worse during their premenstrual period. This does not mean that the changes in their hormones are causing their symptoms, only that this additional stressor has combined with a sensitive body, weakened by the effects of prolonged anxiety, to make it easier to trip the fight-or-flight response.

The connection between a woman's hormones and anxiety is seen also in the fact that for some women, anxiety-related problems first occurred right after the birth of a baby. During this time, a woman's body is still recovering from the intense effort of nurturing the unborn baby and giving birth. The hormones involved in helping a woman's body do this work are still in the process of returning to their normal levels. All of this temporarily produces an increased sensitivity. In addition, there is the stress of adjusting to the changes in one's role in the family as well as the demands of the new baby. If enough of the other factors are present to produce the onset of symptoms, the panic-anxiety cycle can develop.

All of this does *not* mean that men cannot have a sensitive body. Many do. As with women, it helps them "read" others more effectively and is a trait their friends often find appealing. However, it can also make them more vulnerable to the effects of stress and contribute to the development of anxiety-related problems.

Medical Conditions

Because a host of medical conditions can cause anxiety and panic, the first step in working with any anxiety-related problem is to rule out physical causes through a complete examination by a physician. Examples of medical conditions associated with anxiety include cardiovascular problems, asthma, seizure disorder, diabetes, hypothyroidism, and problems with the inner ear. In addition, many other medical conditions can make symptoms worse. One common example is a condition called "Mitral Valve Prolapse", or MVP. This is a minor defect in the heart valve that is found in 5 to 15% of the population. Normally, no medical treatment is required, and 50% of the people with this condition experience no symptoms. For the other half, the main symptom is palpitations, either in the form of premature contractions of the heart or rapid heartbeat. Other symptoms are breathlessness and vague chest pains.

Mary had MVP but had never noticed any MVP symptoms prior to the onset of her panic attacks. However, after her panic attacks developed, she began to notice some of the symptoms commonly associated with MVP. Since Mary was born with this condition, these were probably not new, only something that she was now aware of. After she began to pay close attention to her body, she began to notice these vague but odd sensations and they often triggered thoughts of having a heart attack or panic attack.

Drug Reaction

A wide variety of both prescription and over-the-counter medications can cause anxiety symptoms such as thyroid medications, tranquilizers, sleeping pills, certain blood pressure medications, steroids, allergy and cold medications and, ironically, antidepressants. This is especially true for steroids and antidepressants if they and misused or withdrawn from too quickly. Many herbal and dietary supplements can also cause anxiety symptoms. In addition, common legal and illegal recreational drugs, such as caffeine, alcohol, marijuana, amphetamines, and cocaine, provide another common source of anxiety symptoms.

Caffeine is particularly important since it's often overlooked as a possible problem. Caffeine is a stimulant and, in fact, is the world's most widely used mood-altering drug. Even if you were able to drink coffee or tea without any difficulty prior to the development of your anxiety-related problems, I recommend that you greatly reduce or eliminate caffeine from your diet while you are working through this book. When you are have a problem with anxiety, it just doesn't make sense to put something into your body that can increase anxiety. Also, be sure to check the labels of over-the-counter medications and dietary supplements to see if they contain caffeine.

Many people find that once they have achieved long-term recovery, they can resume drinking moderate amounts of caffeinated drinks without experiencing negative side effects. Others realize that they are caffeine sensitive and that it is best to avoid the drug altogether.

Hyperventilation

Hyperventilation means you are breathing (ventilate: to cause air movement) more rapidly or deeply (hyper: excessively) than is necessary. When you hyperventilate, you set off a host of chemical changes in the blood because you are exhaling more carbon dioxide than normal. This can produce one or more of the following symptoms in less than a minute:

- Heart palpitations, tachycardia (racing heart), heartburn, or chest pain
- Numbness or tingling of the mouth, hands, or feet
- Dizziness, faintness, light-headedness, poor concentration, blurred vision, or a sense of separateness from the body (depersonalization)
- Shortness of breath, asthma, or a choking sensation
- Difficulty swallowing, a lump in the throat, stomach pain, or nausea
- Tension, muscle pains, shaking, or muscle spasms
- Sweating, anxiety, fatigue, weakness, poor sleep, or nightmares

When any of the above are listed as one of the symptoms experienced during a panic attack or high anxiety, I usually find that hyperventilation is playing a role in their anxiety symptoms.

Stress

Stress due to work, school, relationship problems, or to some unusual life event, whether positive or negative, can play an important role in the onset of severe anxiety. Many of the people I work with don't realize this and tend to ignore or give very low priority to any indication that they are tired, ill, hurt emotionally, or stressed. For example, they tend to only be aware of fatigue when it reaches the point of exhaustion. Indeed, learning to pay attention to the signs of stress and developing effective stress management skills are often one of the keys to long-term recovery. Much more is said about stress in later chapters.

Mary's, Robert's, and Kimberly's Simple Explanations

After their first session, Mary, Robert, and Kimberly each developed simple explanations that had three parts:

1. A statement about the factors from childhood that played zn important role in the development and maintenance of the problem symptoms.
2. A statement that described how the initial symptoms developed.
3. A statement that described the forces that caused the symptoms to continue to be a problem.

As you read each explanation, keep in mind that it is meant to summarize the key components that cause and maintain anxiety-related problems. It is not meant to be a detailed explanation. Just as Mary, Robert, and Kimberly gained a deeper understanding of these shorthand explanations over time, you will find new layers of meaning for the explanation you develop as you work through the book.

Mary's Simple Explanation

Childhood Factors:

I grew up in a home where I came to believe the lie that I was stupid and couldn't do anything right. Watching my mother, who was an alcoholic, I also came to believe that the world was dangerous and too much for me to handle. Because all of the adults in my environment were severely damaged, I came to associate intimacy with pain and learned to ignore my own needs. When I was troubled about something, I followed the family rule: "Don't look, don't feel, run away." My mother ran away in alcohol, my father ran away in work, and I ran away in fantasy and sports.

Factors That Caused the Initial Symptoms

My symptoms started during what I now realize was an unusual flight. When the plane dropped, the panic I felt was a normal but intense reaction. I have a reactive body and had been pushing myself just before my next flight. The frightening experience on the previous flight caused me to worry about the plane crashing and the prospect of me dying during my next flight. In fact, I had worked myself up quite a bit by the time we took off. I now recall that I was also coming down with a cold. My initial symptoms were primarily due to a combination of severe hyperventilation, being sick, worry about what might happen on the flight and exhaustion from a tiring workload. This triggered the development of the panic/anxiety cycle and conditioned response anxiety.

Factors That Maintain the Symptoms

Because I didn't understand what had happened and the doctor I went to see couldn't give me a reasonable explanation, I began to worry. I feared that I had some undiagnosed illness or that I might be mentally disturbed in some manner. I began to monitor my body, and whenever I noticed anything that didn't seem right, I told myself lies ("Something's wrong," "I can't handle this," etc.) and ran for safety.

Robert's Simple Explanation

Childhood Factors

I was raised in a terribly abusive family where I developed a very poor self-image and came to believe that people always let you down. I was also bullied at school. Because of this, the association of conflict with danger became a strong conditioned response. I also have a very sensitive body that just doesn't take stress well.

Factors That Caused the Initial Symptoms

My initial symptoms developed during the time when I had just met my current wife and was still having problems with my first wife. I was very sick when the initial choking episode occurred and had just completed a very stressful supervisor training for work. Even though I now realize that I was not in any real danger, my initial thought at that time was that I was dying. I was even thinking that if no one came to my aid, I might not make it.

Factors That Maintain the Symptoms

I tend to be a worrier like my mom. After the choking incident, I recalled the incident where I choked as a child and the thought that people die from having food caught in their throats began to enter my mind whenever I was in a restaurant. I began to see myself choking to death. After a while, just going into a restaurant would make me nervous. As I noticed the anxiety, it would trigger the fearful thoughts. Sometimes, I would become obsessed with a tickling sensation in my throat and would worry, thinking that something was caught there and that it might cause me to choke to death. Essentially, I was telling myself lies about choking, and believing them. This became a conditioned response triggered by being in restaurants or thinking about eating.

Kimberly's Simple Explanation:

Childhood Factors

I grew up in a very competitive family where I learned that I needed to be strong and never show weakness, that second place means nothing, and that perfection is all that counts— all mistakes are unacceptable.

Factors That Caused the Initial Symptoms

I experienced a terrifying assault where I was helpless and unable to protect myself. The event was so intense that my mind simply could not handle the entire picture all at once. In essence, my flashbacks have been little "snapshots" of the event that my mind has been using to process it one piece at a time. In addition, the anxiety that is triggered by things associated with the assault is simply a conditioned response. I will desensitize as I learn to accept these responses as normal and stop reinforcing them.

Factors That Maintain the Symptoms

I made my symptoms worse by telling myself lies about who I am and my reaction to this event ("I'm being weak," "This shouldn't bother me so much," etc.) The truth is that these symptoms are normal and will lessen as time goes by. I am a normal person who has been in an abnormal situation. Part of what has driven this negative view of myself are my childhood beliefs about needing to be strong and never showing weakness. The irrational belief that I should be able to handle anything has also been challenged. Like all humans, I have limits.

Notice how the above experiences are all simply variations on the different types of sad experiences people face. Mary's, Robert's, and Kimberly's anxiety disorders were the normal human reactions of individuals caught in circumstances they didn't understand and were beyond their control.

Summary of Key Ideas

1. People with anxiety-related problems often spend a great deal of time puzzling over why their problems exists. They also engage in negative anticipation ("what if" thinking) where they tell themselves frightening things that are exaggerations or not true.

2. Having a sound and reasonable explanation for how your anxiety-related problem developed and is maintained helps you focus your attention on what you need to do to reach long-term recovery.

3. Body scanning (also called internalization) plays a major role in maintaining symptoms. Noticing normal sensations that have become associated with panic attacks and identifying them as signs of danger can trigger self-generated panic attacks.

4. The answer is E: most anxiety-related problems are caused and maintained by a combination of factors. While the search for a single answer can seem promising, it's usually not productive.

5. Five factors that can interact to generate panic disorder are: a sensitive body, medical conditions, drug reactions, hyperventilation, and stress.

6. When writing a simple explanation, be sure to include the following three areas: childhood factors, factors that caused the initial symptoms, and factors that maintain the symptoms.

Recommended Activities

Continue Keeping a Journaling

In the recommended activities for chapter 3 you were asked to begin keeping a journal. If you haven't started this, I strongly urge you to do so now. Use your journal to develop your simple explanation. Record any thoughts you have about your past and the events that were taking place when your symptoms began. Include your genogram and descriptions of your childhood background. It's also a good idea to record any insights or thoughts you have concerning the work you're doing. Your journal will be a useful tool as you work through the rest of this book.

As mentioned in chapter 3, remember that privacy is essential for journaling. Keeping your writing private helps you write with honesty and openness. When working with issues that have a painful childhood component, it's easy to overlook how they are contributing to your anxiety. Having a place where your insights are recorded allows you to review them periodically so they can be a regular part of how you evaluate events.

When you are confident that you have fully internalized all of the learning required for long-term recovery, you may decide to destroy your journal, or you may want to keep it as a resource you can use in the future as well as a source of encouragement for the progress it records.

Write a Simple Explanation

It's now time for you to develop your own simple explanation. Be sure to include:

1. A written statement about the factors from childhood that played an important role in the development and maintenance of the problem symptoms.
2. How the initial symptoms developed (be sure to list all of the sources of stress that were occurring as well as childhood factors that may have played a role).
3. The forces that cause the symptoms to continue to be a problem.

Take your time in developing this explanation. It may help to review the family background and childhood descriptions of Mary, Robert, and Kimberly in chapters 2 and 4 and compare them with the explanations they developed in this chapter. You will see that all three thought of new factors that they hadn't realized were important when they first described their backgrounds and symptoms to me. Like them, you will also experience new insights about yourself and your background as you develop your own explanation.

In developing your simple explanation, avoid the use of psychological terms and self-help "buzz words". Instead, state your ideas in plain everyday English. If it's difficult for you to give a clear and simple explanation, you probably haven't yet gained a good understanding of why your symptoms developed and why they continue to be a problem.

If you find it difficult to develop your simple explanation, review the previous chapters and ask someone you know and trust to help you. If you are in therapy, ask your therapist for help. If you are in a self-help group that you feel is trustworthy, ask the group for help. Use the explanations that Mary, Robert, and Kimberly developed as models. Four additional examples of simple explanations from other people I've worked with are given below.

The Simple Explanation of a Person with a Fear of Hospitals

Childhood Factors

> As a child, I had lots of scary experiences connected with doctors due to my asthma. I also didn't think too well of myself because my parents were always criticizing me.

Factors That Caused the Initial Symptoms

> When I tried some marijuana, I had a terrifying drug reaction during which I became paranoid and believed

I was dying. When I went to the emergency room, the staff was very critical of me when I told them I had tried marijuana. Some of what they said scared me very much. This reactivated many of my childhood fears and caused a conditioned response to things connected with hospitals and doctors.

Factors That Maintain the Symptoms

Whenever I'm in a medical setting and begin to get anxious I tell myself the following lies: "The anxiety symptoms mean that I've damaged my body beyond repair." "I can't control what's going on." "I'm helpless." "The doctors are going to be able to see how stupid I was in trying that drug, and they will think badly of me." None of all that is true. In fact, the exact opposite of each is reality.

The Simple Explanation of a Person with Social Phobia and Panic Disorder

Childhood Factors

I have a very sensitive body and was always shy and timid as a child. Because I didn't have many friends or do much socially as a child, I didn't gain the social skills that most people have.

Factors That Caused the Initial Symptoms

In the seventh grade I was very worried about my changing body and awkwardness. I considered myself to be ugly and stupid and believed that everybody thought poorly of me. While in English class, I was supposed to give an oral book report. I became so nervous that I began to shake. Thinking that everyone was laughing at me (even though they weren't), I ran from the room and soon began to hyperventilate. The symptoms were very frightening, and from that day on I began to avoid talking to any type of group and fear that something isn't right with me.

Factors That Maintain the Symptoms

For years I've told myself things that are not true. I've also become an expert at noticing any funny sensation that occurs in my body. Whenever I notice something that I've labeled as abnormal, I tell myself the following: "I'm going to have a panic attack and it will be terrible. People will notice my anxiety and think that I'm 'weird." It's these types of fearful thoughts that produce and maintain my anxiety and panic.

The Simple Explanation of a Person with Panic Disorder

Childhood Factors

I was raised in a large family where I got lost in the shuffle. I was abused when I was young, both physically and verbally. Because of this, I developed the beliefs that I was tainted, broken, and somehow substandard. I also have a body with an inherited genetic weakness (irritable bowel syndrome). The way I learned to deal with problems was to apply the rule "Don't look, don't feel, run away."

Factors That Caused the Initial Symptoms

As a young adult I developed physical symptoms due to my sensitive body and the stress of dealing with death (the deaths of three people close to me in one year). My initial symptoms were a normal reaction to stress where I hyperventilated because of real life events that were difficult to face.

Factors That Maintain My Symptoms

Because I didn't understand what was happening and didn't want to deal with the emotional issues that were going on, I created a boogie man (my anxiety symptoms). Whenever I noticed any unusual sensation, I told myself lies (I'm dying, I can't breathe, etc.) and ran from the boogie man.

The Simple Explanation of a Person with Panic Disorder

Childhood Factors

I grew up in a home with a controlling father and a very nonassertive and passive mother. I learned that conflict was to be avoided, and it was important to hide feelings, be compliant, and maintain the facade of being the perfect child. The message from my father was I didn't measure up unless I did things his way. I also learned that it was dangerous to take risks or give opinions.

Factors That Caused the Initial Symptoms

I married a controlling and verbally abusive man, and I was very passive and compliant. Together, we presented the facade of the happy couple throughout my childbearing years. Then, because I couldn't take it anymore, I divorced him. I suffered a massive stress reaction after becoming a single parent; working part-time and going to paralegal school; moving back to California; and failing to receive support payments from my ex-husband.

Factors That Maintain the Symptoms

Because I had been trained not to deal with things directly and needed to maintain the facade of being in control, I suppressed feelings, focused on my symptoms instead of the life issues causing them, and developed panic attacks and severe anxiety.

CHAPTER 6

Symptom-Management Skills

This chapter presents the four basic symptom-management skills Mary, Robert, and Kimberly learned during their first and second sessions.

- Cue-controlled relaxation response training
- Breathing Techniques
- Coping self-statements
- Distraction/externalization

As with most of the clients I've worked with, Mary, Robert, and Kimberly each had some knowledge of these skills. However, their skill set was incomplete. Mary had practiced meditation. Robert had been told he was hyperventilating and was taking deep breaths to try to control it. He did not know that this actually had the opposite effect and increased his symptoms. All three had some knowledge of coping self-statements, but were using them with only mixed results. Reviewing each skill in detail allowed Mary, Robert, and Kimberly to use them more effectively for managing their symptoms.

If you are already familiar with these skills, you may be tempted to skim over this chapter and move on to the next one. Instead, I encourage you to take your time as you work through the chapter and reflect on how you are currently using each skill as you read about it. You may find ways to fine tune what you are doing that makes each skill more effective.

Cue-Controlled Relaxation Response

Herbert Benson used the term "relaxation response" to describe a state of deep-muscle relaxation that was triggered by some set method such as progressive relaxation, bio-feedback, self-hypnosis, and meditation. When the relaxation response is associated with a cue, such as a simple physical gesture, a word, or a mental image, it becomes a cue-controlled relaxation response.

One of the key features of anxiety-related problems is the association of normal, everyday activities and situations with danger that produces an anxiety generating conditioned response as described in chapter 3. The conditioned response generated by this association triggers anxiety whenever a person does an activity or is in a situation associated with this conditioned response. A person with a well-developed a cue-controlled relaxation response can use it to reduce the anxiety triggered by an anxiety producing conditioned response.

While this sounds great in theory, keep in mind that you probably have a very strong set of anxiety producing conditioned responses that have been reinforced for several months or years. When you first start practicing cue-controlled relaxation, it is much weaker than these anxiety producing conditioned responses. Because of this, a cue controlled relaxation response may only produce a slight reduction of your anxiety. However, this small reduction, when added to the calming effect of the other tools, usually helps a person keep anxiety at a manageable level. With practice and time, the cue-controlled relaxation response becomes a stronger and more effective tool. Appendix 4 describes several different methods you can use to develop a cue-controlled.

I routinely give the clients I work with a recording that helps them develop cue-controlled relaxation. The recording uses a standard procedure called progressive relaxation to produce deep relaxation. During this time, the person places the first two fingers and thumb of either hand together to associate this action with the deep relaxation. With practice, the touching of the fingers and thumb together creates a simple cue controlled relaxation response that can be used in anxiety producing situations. While other actions such as a word or image in place of the physical cue could be used, I use the fingers and thumb cue because it is easy to do in most situations and is something others don't notice. A free download of this recording is available on my website: www.rpeurifoy.com.

Breathing Techniques

Chapter 5 lists the common symptoms caused by hyperventilation and describes hyperventilation as breathing more rapidly or deeply than is necessary for a given situation. It is often the result of excessive upper-chest breathing, mouth breathing because of medical or physical problems, or breath holding.

Take a moment to see how you are breathing. Lie down, and place one hand on your chest and one hand just above your navel. Take two or three breaths that are slightly deeper than normal and see which hand moves. If the hand on your chest moves, you are using upper-chest breathing. If the hand just above your navel moves you are breathing with your diaphragm.

Keep in mind that both of these forms of breathing are normal. Upper-chest breathing is normal when you are exercising or excited. It is designed to help your body get plenty of oxygen. The body uses diaphragmatic breathing when there is little demand for activity. Unfortunately, many people, like Robert, use upper-chest breathing as their primary method of breathing, even when they are sitting or relaxed. Although it is unclear why some people become habitual upper-chest breathers, it may simply be that people who continually feel threatened by common, everyday situations trigger this breathing pattern via the activation of the fight-or-flight response.

Another explanation may stem from our culture's obsession with thin bodies and flat stomachs. Some people, particularly appearance-conscious adolescents, consciously "suck in" their stomachs in order to conform to this cultural image. This results in the habitual, unconscious tensing of the abdominal muscles. Since you cannot tense your abdomen and use diaphragmatic breathing at the same time, the body begins to use upper-chest breathing as its primary breathing pattern. Wearing tight-fitting clothes that restrict the movement of the diaphragm can also contribute to upper-chest breathing. Whatever the cause, Robert had become a habitual upper-chest breather and was, thus, constantly hyperventilating.

In addition to being an upper-chest breather, Robert also held his breath whenever he was in a tense situation or dealing with strong emotions. When he resumed breathing, he would either sigh or yawn, which caused a slight tingling sensation to flow down his body, the result of the momentary change in the balance of oxygen and carbon dioxide in his blood stream —a normal response. However, because this sensation had become so associated with the severe hyperventilation he had been experiencing, Robert would notice this sensation, see it as the onset of a panic attack, and begin the negative self-talk that intensified his anxiety.

Breath holding like Robert's is a simple conditioned response that usually is learned in childhood. If someone yells at you or hits you, the natural tendency is to hold your breath. Robert's parents were constantly yelling at him. His father periodically hit him. Because of this, any type of conflict in adulthood "felt" like danger and caused Robert to hold his breath. There are three ways in which hyperventilation symptoms can be reduced. The first is known as the paper bag technique.

Paper Bag Technique

With the paper bag technique, you carry a paper bag with you and breathe into it whenever you experience the symptoms of severe hyperventilation. Since your breathing is regulated by carbon dioxide, the rapid increase of carbon dioxide in the bag as the oxygen is used up slows your breathing. If a paper bag is not handy, cup your hands over your mouth and nose and breathe into them. The paper bag technique works, but it is awkward and can be embarrassing to use in public.

Combat Tactical Breathing

A second technique was developed by the military and is known as combat tactical breathing or more simply as either combat or tactical breathing. In addition to the military, this technique is also used by first responders and athletes to help them focus, gain control and manage a distressing situation. Combat breathing is done by taking three to five breaths in the following manner. If you are in a situation that allows it, visualize each number as you count.

1. Breathe in slowly through your nose and count: 1, 2, 3, 4.
2. Stop and hold your breath as you count: 1, 2, 3, 4.
3. Exhale slowly through your mouth as you count: 1, 2, 3, 4.

Relaxed Diaphragmatic Breathing

Another technique that is similar to combat breathing is relaxed diaphragmatic. With this technique you learn what relaxed diaphragmatic breathing feels like and practice it when you're in anxiety producing situations. Because this is a more involved process, details on how to develop this ability are given in the "Recommended activities" section at the end of this chapter. The advantage of using relaxed diaphragmatic breathing instead of the other two techniques is that you can use it anywhere without others knowing. Once mastered, it's a great way to prevent hyperventilation from becoming severe when used at the first signs of anxiety.

Coping Self-Statements

Coping self-statements are statements you say or think to yourself that help you cope with a difficult situation. They are an essential tool you can use to counter the negative self-talk that accompanies anxiety. Negative self-talk associated with anxiety usually centers around the following ideas:

- Something dangerous is happening to me. These symptoms are a sign of some severe mental or physical problem.
- I won't be able to function because of these symptoms.
- These symptoms will cause me to do something embarrassing.
- People will notice my problem and think poorly of me.

Let's look at how coping self-statements can be used to combat each of these fears.

These Symptoms Are a Sign of Danger

As mentioned in chapter 5, the first step in working with any anxiety-related problem is to rule out possible "medical" causes through a complete physical examination. Clients I work with have usually done this before they see me. This means that the unpleasant symptoms they are experiencing are normal physiological processes and do not signal any form of physical danger. Unfortunately, it's often difficult for people experiencing severe anxiety is convince themselves that their symptoms are not dangerous. Indeed, one of the keys to long-term recovery is the conviction that your symptoms, while frightening, are harmless.

I Won't Be Able to Function Because of These Symptoms

Mary, Robert, and Kimberly all had many well-developed images of being incapacitated by their anxiety. By recalling these frightening images over and over, they became a reality in their minds. I find it very useful to point out that by the time they see me, the vast majority of clients have already experienced the worst episodes of anxiety they will ever experience. While they may experience episodes in the future that are as intense, the most frightening and intense episodes of anxiety tend to occur early in the course of an anxiety-related problem when people have the least number of coping skills and understanding of what is happening. By the time I see them, they have developed at least some coping strategies and symptom-management skills on their own or from a book or previous therapy.

These Symptoms Will Cause Me to Do Something Embarrassing

People routinely believe that they will say something crazy or do something inappropriate. Again, the knowledge that you've already experienced your worst anxiety is often helpful to remember. Because you did not act grossly inappropriately during previous episodes of intense anxiety, you've already demonstrated that you won't do anything bizarre in the future.

People Will Notice My Problem and Think Poorly of Me

This fear is often a reflection of childhood fears of rejection and abandonment. Mary, Robert, and Kimberly all experienced rejection from their parents. They also had beliefs about being inferior to others. Their symptoms reinforced childhood fears not only about being somehow odd and inferior, but about others rejecting them because of their inferiority.

Consider how you would respond to someone experiencing severe anxiety. You would probably be compassionate and try to help this person. Likewise, this is how most others would respond to you. Besides, most of the people I work with have become experts at presenting a good front when they're anxious.

Remember that your sensitivity means you tend to notice more than the average person. Your struggle with anxiety has also made you hypersensitive to signs of anxiety. Most of the people around you lack your sensitivity and are absorbed in their own affairs. So, even if you are one of the few who shake or display other outward signs of anxiety, people who notice are probably too absorbed in their own lives to give it much thought.

Examples of Coping Self-Statements

After Mary, Robert, and Kimberly developed a set of coping self-statements, they wrote them on an index card and carried them wherever they went. Since all of them tended to forget their coping self-statements during times of excessive anxiety, the cards became a tool they could use to remind themselves of the truth of their situation. Here are the cards they created:

Mary's Card

Anxiety is not dangerous; it's just uncomfortable.

I can be anxious and still function effectively.

Don't forget to trigger the relaxation response and take relaxed diaphragmatic breaths. They calm me.

There is nothing wrong with me. These sensations are just a conditioned response.

I've always been able to manage my anxiety and act normal in the past, even when experiencing my worst episodes. I will be able to manage it now.

People are so absorbed in their own lives that they aren't really concerned with what I'm experiencing. Even if they did notice that I'm anxious, they've got other things to think about.

Robert's Card

I am safe, my anxiety is not dangerous.

The anxiety I'm experiencing is just a conditioned response that is being intensified because of the job stress I'm under and the lies I've been telling myself.

The original choking incident was an unusual situation. I have told myself lies about what it meant and my symptoms continued because I began to watch my body and repeat the old lies to myself.

This tickling in the throat and occasional cough is just a type of conditioned response. It will lessen as I desensitize myself.

My body is designed to eat. I've been eating all of my life.

Stay focused on the truth, use your combat breathing and distract yourself.

Kimberly's Card

The flashbacks I'm experiencing are simply "snapshots" of the assault that my mind is using to process the trauma.

I am a normal person who was in an abnormal situation

The anxiety I occasionally experience over things connected with the assault are a simple conditioned response danger signal. There is no longer any danger.

These symptoms won't hurt me and will lessen with time.

Externalization/Distraction

In the last chapter, you learned that one of the key components of the anxiety/panic cycle is an excessive focus on the body. One of the ways to break this cycle is to distract yourself by shifting your focus away from symptoms to something positive or neutral. Since focusing on the body is a form of internalization, the best form of distraction is externalization, focusing your awareness on something outside the body.

There are many different simple forms of externalization. Many people find it useful to focus on their surroundings when they are anxious. Mary, for example, would fix her attention on the design of a nearby wall or the clothing of people around her. Robert found that listening attentively to random conversations worked well for him. Kimberly tried a tactile approach, carrying gum with her and feeling the texture of the gum wrapper. She also liked to feel the texture of her clothes or the steering wheel of her car.

Kimberly also found it helpful, when practical, to change her immediate surroundings. For example, if she was inside, she would go outside; if she was sitting, she would stand up; if she was in the living room, she would go into the kitchen.

Simple mental activities that require concentration can also be an effective means of distraction. When Robert became anxious, he thought of things at work or home that needed to be done and planned them out in detail. Mary, who liked to sing, found it helpful to sing when alone or around people and to recall the lyrics to a song. These are more complex forms of distraction and can be difficult to do when you are very anxious, but with practice, and when used at the first signs of anxiety, they can be very effective.

Mary, Robert, and Kimberly discovered that they experienced fewer symptoms when they were busy with some sort of physical activity. A physical activity helps to keep you focused outside of your body. When Kimberly became anxious at home, she discovered that washing dishes or cleaning something helped. Most people find that work involving some kind of physical activity, even if it is just with the hands, is better than purely mental activity.

Mary, Robert, and Kimberly each found that conversation provided an effective means of distraction. With Mary and Robert, only conversations with someone they knew was useful, while Kimberly found that even light banter with strangers was an effective distraction.

Externalization and distraction are more effective if you first stop and tell yourself the truth about your symptoms using your coping self-statements. An Irish adage says, "If you run from a ghost it will keep chasing you, but if you run toward it, it will disappear." When you've been telling yourself lies about anxiety—things such as "It's dangerous," or "It will make me lose control"—you need to stop and challenge the lies, then state the truth. By doing this, you are "facing the ghost" of anxiety. If, when you are anxious, you immediately try to externalize or distract, without first stating the truth, they become just another way in which you are running from the ghost.

Summary of Key Ideas

1. Four basic symptom-management skills are cue-controlled relaxation, breathing techniques, coping self-statements, and distraction/externalization.

2. Many of the unpleasant symptoms associated with panic are due to hyperventilation. The three breathing techniques work well, especially when used during the early stages of anxiety.

3. Four key ideas to include in coping self-statements are: "Anxiety is not dangerous"; "I can experience anxiety and still function effectively"; "Most people are not sensitive like me, so they probably won't notice my symptoms"; and "Most people are so busy with their own lives that, even if they notice anything, they won't care about what I'm experiencing."

4. It's useful to write several coping self-statements on index cards and memorize them. You can also carry them with you and use them to remind yourself of the truth when you are anxious.

5. The best form of distraction is externalization, focusing on something outside of your body.

6. Distraction that involves physical activity is more effective than mental distraction.

7. Distraction works best if you first stop and tell yourself the truth about your symptoms with your coping self-statements.

Recommended Activities

Begin Developing Cue-controlled Relaxation

Appendix 4 outlines several standard procedures for developing a relaxation response. As you use them, place the first two fingers and thumb of either hand together. This will associate this simple physical act with your relaxation response. This cue usually takes several practice sessions to become associated with the relaxation response. However, once this happens, it begins to become a helpful skill that will become stronger with continued practice.

Practice Combat Tactical Breathing

Practice combat tactical breathing a few times when you are not anxious so you know how to do it in an anxiety provoking situation.

Learn Relaxed Diaphragmatic Breathing

Each night before you go to sleep, spend one to two minutes doing the following:

1. Lie flat on your back and place one hand on your chest and the other a little above your navel.
2. Close your eyes and imagine the air going all the way down to your navel.

Your goal is to breathe so that your lower hand moves up and down gently in a relaxed manner. Your chest may also move a little, but most of the movement should be from the diaphragm. The goal is to take small, relaxed breaths rather than big breaths. As you practice, notice that there is a slight pause just after your exhalation and before your inhalation (inhalation, exhalation, pause, inhalation, exhalation, pause). Depending on your size, this pause can last from one to several seconds. Breathing with this gentle, unforced pause is sometimes called relaxed pause breathing.

Continue practicing relaxed diaphragmatic breathing until you can (1) tell whether you're using upper-chest or diaphragmatic breathing without placing your hands on your chest and abdomen, and (2) can easily take relaxed diaphragmatic breaths.

While the majority of people I work with find diaphragmatic breathing easy to learn, Robert found it difficult when he first tried it. If you experience some difficulty, try sucking in the abdominal region as you exhale. Then simply relax and do nothing as you inhale. Your abdominal region will naturally expand outward on its own. Remember, however, that your goal is to exert very little effort or attention in order to breathe diaphragmatically.

Your body already knows how to breathe this way. In fact, your body uses diaphragmatic breathing each night when you are in deep sleep, so you are not learning something new. You are only developing the ability to trigger something that your body already does. Once Robert understood this, he quickly mastered the ability to breathe diaphragmatically.

One commonly mistaken idea about breathing is that you should take a deep breath when you are anxious. When I first discussed diaphragmatic breathing with Mary, she reported that she already knew how to do it. However, since she was continuing to experience much light-headedness and a "lack of air," it was evident that hyperventilation was still a problem. When I asked her to show me what she was doing, she took several very large diaphragmatic breaths.

Taking large diaphragmatic breaths, like rapid upper-chest breathing, increases hyperventilation symptoms. So, while Mary could easily take diaphragmatic breaths, she was using this ability in a way that increased rather than decreased her symptoms. The key to using diaphragmatic breathing is to take relaxed breaths that are similar to those you take when resting. Within a week Mary had mastered this skill and it greatly reduced the amount of hyperventilation symptoms she experienced.

While diaphragmatic breathing is a powerful skill, it is important to avoid becoming overly concerned with your breathing. Keep your practice sessions short, just a minute or less. Do not make this hard work. You have been breathing all of your life and, as has already been mentioned, your body already knows how to take relaxed diaphragmatic breaths. You are merely learning how to do it consciously. If you experience a sense of lightheadedness or one of the other hyperventilation symptoms, you are working too hard at the exercise. Take smaller and more relaxed breaths.

After you have mastered diaphragmatic breathing while lying down, practice two or three times a day while standing or sitting. You may find it a little more difficult at first, but with practice, you will find breathing with your diaphragm to be easy and your normal method of breathing, even if you are a habitual upper-chest breather like Robert.

Once you learn how to use this skill, take three or four slow, relaxed diaphragmatic breaths at the first signs of anxiety. You can also do this before anything that might be anxiety provoking such as a presentation or interview.

Create Several Coping Self-Statements

Create four to six coping self-statements of your own and write them on an index card you can carry with you. Begin to refer to them whenever you experience anxiety. If you like any of those created by Mary, Robert, or Kimberly, use them exactly as written or, if their statements do not fit your personality or life situation, change the wording to compose new ones that do apply. It is important that your coping self-statements have power and meaning for you.

Create a "Summary Card"

In addition to your coping self-statement card, create a card that summarizes your basic anxiety symptom-management skills. Here is an example of one I routinely use with clients:

Skills Summary Card

1. Use the cue that triggers your relaxation response.
2. Take three or four relaxed diaphragmatic breaths.
3. Read your coping self-statements.
4. Distract yourself; externalize.

CHAPTER 7

Distorted Thinking

Within three weeks Mary, Robert, and Kimberly had all developed simple explanations for their conditions and were beginning to gain some mastery of the four basic symptom-management skills presented in the last chapter. As a result, they began to move into what, in chapter 1, is called the "first level of recovery", or "basic symptom control." Even though they were still having acute symptoms, they were beginning to experience their first taste of success in managing anxiety. The next step in their treatment was to help them identify and challenge habitual thinking patterns that contributed to the development of their debilitating anxiety and supported the maintenance of their symptoms.

Distorted Thinking

The way you think is, for the most part, a habit pattern that is not very different from the hundreds of other habit patterns you've developed during your life. Much of your thought is characterized by silent inner conversations you have with yourself called self-talk. Sometimes you are aware of your self-talk. However, much of your self-talk is done in an automatic and habitual manner. It's as if a particular situation triggers a specific habitual response that includes a well-rehearsed script that you repeat to yourself.

Thoughts that distort reality in some way are called cognitive distortions or simply distorted thinking. Thoughts that help you look at your situation more realistically and identify the choices you have in a given situation are called rational self-talk. With practice rational self-talk not only becomes a powerful tool for calming yourself, but it also helps you become more effective in daily life. Since my first book discusses distorted thinking in great detail, this chapter only focuses on the five forms that have caused the most problems for clients I've worked with.

Should/must thinking

Should/must thinking describes thoughts that reflect preferences and desires that have become rigid rules. The most common form is a thought or statement characterized by the words *should, must, have to,* or *can't.* When the rule expressed by this type of thinking is broken or when the desired outcome is not met, it not only causes strong negative emotions but you also tend to become problem-focused. This means that you focus on how awful the situation is and fail to consider what you can do to make things better.

The key to changing should/must thinking is to realize there is nothing that you have to do. People often object when I say this and respond with statements such as, "I have to go to work!" When I then tell them, "No, you don't have to go to work," they go on to tell me various reasons why they "have" to go to work. I would then respond by pointing out that they are choosing to go to work because they either want to obtain certain things or avoid certain negative consequences. The bottom line is that *life is a series of choices that we make based on what we think will help us gain the things we want and avoid the things we don't want.*

Whenever you notice yourself thinking about or stating your wants or preferences with words like *should, must, have to* or *can't,* practice substituting the phrases *I like, I want,* or *I prefer.* Using our example of being on time, you could restate the "should/must" statement as: "I like to be on time," "I want to be on time" or "I prefer to be on time." Statements like these are not only more realistic, but they also help you to remember that your rules are based on your choices and preferences. They are not universal absolutes. Here is an example of self-talk that Robert used when he found himself becoming anxious about running late for an appointment.

> "While I want to be there on time, I don't have to be on time. With this traffic, I'm probably going to be a little late. There is nothing I can do about it. So just relax and get there when you can. I can relax and call my friend. He'll understand."

Gaining skill in noticing your distorted thinking and answering it with a rational challenge helps you to feel more in control of your life. In areas of your life dominated by should/must thinking, it feels like an invisible parent is making you do things you don't want to do. Returning to our earlier example, consider the difference in how it feels to say, "I have to be on time" instead of simply saying, "I like to be on time," or "I want to be on time."

When you begin using the language of choice, you are no longer a slave to rules that you have to blindly follow. Instead, you become the one deciding what is best for you. Substituting, "want", "like" or "prefer" for your "shoulds" and "musts" also helps you to both experience a greater sense of calm in situations where things happen that you don't like and be more effective when choosing your response.

Circular Questioning

While should/must thinking tends to be easy to spot, there is a related form of distorted thinking I call circular questioning that is harder to see in oneself. Circular questioning is the act of asking a series of questions over and over without any real attempt to answer them. When you watch people using circular questioning it appears as though they have "short-circuited" in some fashion. Actually, they have only become confused because reality is not conforming to one or more of their beliefs about how the world "should" be.

Individuals suffering from anxiety-related problems often spend much time engaged in circular questioning about their condition with thoughts or self-talk that usually starts with "why" or "how". For example, a person who has done something that was regretted later may dwell on the misbehavior and think:

> "How could I have done that? I don't understand why I acted that way.

Because circular questioning is so common, let's look at an example of circular questioning that Robert engaged in when a friend disappointed him.

> "I just don't understand why Ernesto didn't call like he said he would. He's usually not like that. It doesn't make sense. Why would he do this when he knows how important this was to me?"

As with many, Robert believed that everyone should live by the same rules he used to govern his own life. One of those rules was "you should always do what you say you're going to do." His circular questioning was a reflection of the confusion caused when his should/must rule did not match the reality that Ernesto did not do what he said he was going to do.

After listening to Robert's circular questioning, I asked him, "Tell me why you think he did that." Like most people who are asked to provide an answer to the "whys" of circular questioning,

Robert had no immediate answer. However, after a minute of thought and a little prompting he quickly began to generate numerous possibilities. Here are a few. See if you can think of others.

- Maybe something important came up.
- Maybe Ernesto didn't realize how important it was to me.
- There might have been some sort of misunderstanding.

In addition, we could add at least two more: Some people make agreements they have no intention of honoring because it's an easy way to avoid conflict. Others have unresolved issues from childhood that prevent them from following through on what they say. What a wonderful world it would be, if everyone followed Robert's rule and always did what they said they were going to do. Unfortunately, they don't and we need to decide how we're going to respond when this happens.

Whenever you notice yourself engaged in circular questioning, remind yourself that it is simply an indication that you are having difficulty accepting the fact that some aspect of reality is not meeting your desires or expectations. When this occurs, remind yourself that reality is often different from what you would like it to be and redirect your focus to how you should respond.

The next time you find yourself engaged in circular questioning, do the following.

- Answer your questions.
- Decide how you are going to respond.

Here's how Robert applied this two-step approach to his circular questioning about Ernesto:

Let's answer the "whys." I know Ernesto is very busy and has a lot on his mind with his sick wife. He probably just forgot. I also know that while calling is a big deal to me, it probably isn't as important to Ernesto.

Now, let's focus on how I can respond. While I wish Ernesto would be more responsible, he is the way he is and there is nothing I can do to change it. If I want to maintain the friendship, I need to accept that he's going to be thoughtless from time to time. This means I cannot depend on him to respond the way I want him to respond. If I cannot accept this, I need to find new friends who respond in a way that meets my expectations. For now, I'll just give him a call and see what happens.

Magnification/Minimization

Magnification is the term used to describe the act of exaggerating or "magnifying" an event into something bigger or worse than it actually is. This is also called "catastrophizing" because a minor difficulty or problem is transformed into a catastrophe. While there are many ways in which people exaggerate the seriousness of events, words like "terrible," "awful," and "horrible" are often used. One common phrase that is associated with magnification is, "I can't stand it when . . ."

Whenever Robert felt anything in his throat that seemed odd, he would magnify it into a life-threatening event. Whenever Kimberly considered the possibility of not working at her old position because she no longer felt safe there, she magnified it into a major personal defeat. Here are some examples of catastrophic self-talk used when describing a panic attack:

- It's terrible when I get anxious.
- The feeling is absolutely awful.
- I just can't stand it.

As was mentioned in the discussion on coping self-statements, this type of self-talk increases symptoms and makes you feel worse than you would otherwise. It is important to understand that you can stand anxiety. Indeed, one of the goals of desensitization is to prove to yourself that you can be anxious and still function. Although anxiety can be very uncomfortable, you can learn how to manage it and return to normal activities. To say you cannot stand anxiety is to believe a lie. The fact is you have withstood it; you have survived it.

Minimization is often called "discounting" and describes the diminishing or belittling of positive aspects about yourself or things connected with you. For example, when I first pointed out how much calmer Kimberly was at home and in a variety of situations outside of the home, she responded with:

> "I'm really not that much better. If I was, I'd quit getting so nervous every time I go to a mall and see someone who looks like the student who assaulted me."

Kimberly's perfectionism made it difficult for her to acknowledge small improvements. In the beginning, the only thing that counted was to have no symptoms.

Negative Anticipation (What-if Thinking) and Emotional Reasoning

Another type of distorted thinking common in people with anxiety-related problems is what I call "What-If" thinking which is more formally known as negative anticipation. This type of thinking is characterized by imagining a host of frightening possibilities. For example, when planning to go somewhere, Mary, who feared the symptoms caused by hyperventilation would often think, "What if I start to breathe funny." This would then trigger the thought, "I might pass out." This led to a host of frightening thoughts and images of passing out along with negative consequences that might follow.

When challenging 'what if' thinking it's important to look at your track record. How often has this actually happened in the past? This is often difficult because 'what if' thinking tends to be accompanied by emotional reasoning. Emotional reasoning is when you use emotion to evaluate the possibility of something happening. In other words, when a thought triggers strong negative emotions, a person then believes that it is likely to be true. Unfortunately, these emotions are usually being fueled by anxiety and are not based on reality.

When I ask a person who is thinking that they might pass out, "How likely is this?" They usually respond that it's highly likely. When I then ask, "How many times have you actually passed out?" they usually respond, "I've never passed out." So, based on emotion, it is very likely. However, based on past experience, it very unlikely.

The key point is that "Feelings are not facts". Sometimes, they come from rational thinking, and other times they come from very distorted and irrational thinking. You always have to evaluate your feelings with the reasoning part of your mind.

Challenge what-if thinking by answering the following four questions:

1. Based on reality, rather than emotional reasoning, how likely is this?
2. How bad would it actually be if this happened? When considering this question, rate it on a scale of 1 to 10 with ten representing truly tragic events such as losing someone you love or dying from a painful wasting disease. When considered in this light, most things become passing inconveniences rather than tragedies.
3. What is my plan to prevent this from happening?
4. What is my plan for coping with this if it were to happen?

Let's continue with the example of a Mary who was dwelling on the frightening thought, "I might pass out."

1. How likely is this? Based on the past, the odds are very low that this will happen because I've never passed out.
2. How bad would it be? My emotions tell me that this would be the worst thing I can think of. However, on my scale of 1 to 10 this is only a two, maybe a three. After all, hyperventilation doesn't really cause any lasting harm. If I were to pass out, I would only be out for a few minutes as my body readjusted the oxygen and CO_2 levels back to normal. The main consequence of passing out would be embarrassment. While embarrassment is unpleasant, it is bearable and way down the scale from truly catastrophic things that could happen.
3. What is my plan to prevent this from happening? I know I do better when I use my relaxed diaphragmatic breathing at the first sign of hyperventilation. I can also carry my coping self-statements cards in case my mind starts to race. It also helps if I eat something before going out.
4. What would I do if it were to happen? First, I'd want to sit down so I don't hurt myself. Second, if there are people around, I could tell them, "I'm OK, Just give me a few minutes and I'll be fine."

After thinking through a what-if thought like this in detail, compress it into a short coping self-statement you can use to counter the thought whenever it occurs. This is especially useful for what-if thoughts that are particularly troublesome. Here's how Mary summarized her thoughts about passing out on a card:

1. I've never passed out so it is very unlikely that this will occur – stop your emotional reasoning.
2. It would not be the end of the world so stop catastrophizing.

3. I know how to do relaxed diaphragmatic breathing and I do better when I chew gum.
4. I know what to say and can take care of myself.

Challenging Irrational and Negative Self-Talk

To all outward appearances, prior to the onset of their symptoms, Mary, Robert, and Kimberly were living what seemed like normal lives. They were employed and going about their everyday activities like anyone else. On reflection, however, all three saw how this normal-looking exterior hid the fact that distorted thinking was playing a major role in their everyday lives. More importantly, distorted thinking played a subtle yet key role in the development of their anxiety-related problems and an even greater role in maintaining them.

Once the initial episodes of anxiety occur, distorted thinking tends to become even more pronounced. One of the roles it takes is to reinforce the negative beliefs and associations from childhood. Thus, Mary's childhood belief that she was inferior to others was confirmed by the fact that she now couldn't handle even simple trips outside of her town. Robert's childhood belief that something was wrong with him was confirmed by the fact that he was unable to eat anything other than baby food. Kimberly's childhood belief that mistakes were unacceptable transformed the student's unpredictable assault into a "mistake" that she "had allowed to happen," which, in turn, became a nightmare that was even worse than the assault.

To achieve long-term recovery, Mary, Robert, and Kimberly had to learn how to identify and effectively challenge the cognitive distortions that had become habits. Here is an example of a rational challenge Kimberly developed:

Kimberly's Negative Self-Talk about the Possibility of Transferring to a New Position

I can't stand it when I think about going back to my old position. I don't know why I can't get it together and go back to the way I used to be. Instead, I keep thinking about running away to a new position.

Kimberly's Rational Challenge

First of all, I can stand it when I think about what happened. While it still makes me anxious, I am able to think about it, and continue to function. I don't become comatose or paralyzed. I also know that the anxiety I feel when I think about going back is an important message. Maybe it is time to move on. I'm different because of the assault. The fact that I'm mortal is much more real to me. I also realize that it's possible for a stronger person to overpower me. I'm not invincible. Transferring to a new position is not a sign of failure. It's simply an acknowledgment of the fact that I no longer want to expose myself to dangers that I used to ignore. People make choices like this all the time. It's just a reflection of maturity and a desire to be in a less dangerous environment and nothing more.

In addition to confronting distorted thinking you identify, it's often useful to include a rational challenge to the core beliefs that generated the negative self-talk. Here is how Kimberly did this:

Kimberly's Negative Self-talk Concerning the Assault

I should have known this student was dangerous. I don't know how I could have been so careless.

Kimberly's Rational Challenge

Although I knew that this student, like all the others, had potential for violence, there was nothing in his chart or file that indicated he was more dangerous than the others. I took all the usual precautions that had been sufficient in the past. The simple truth is this was an unusual situation and this student was bigger and stronger than me. There was also no help available. If there is any responsibility to be assigned, it is to the lack of staffing at that site. I did the best I could do in those circumstances. It simply wasn't enough. I am not God. I don't know everything that is going on, and I don't always have the ability to do what I would like to do.

The thing that makes this such a big problem is my desire never to be weak. I know this comes from the constant competition with my dad and his constant put-downs whenever I made a mistake or showed weakness. He was unreasonable. Unfortunately, I've internalized him and can be unreasonable with myself. It's OK to make mistakes and be human. I certainly don't want to go through life the way he has.

Summary of Key Ideas

1. Everyone has habitual ways in which they process information that distorts reality. This chapter discussed the five forms that are most common in clients I work with.
2. Should/must thinking describes thoughts that reflect preferences and desires that have become ridge rules. The most common form is a thought or statement characterized by the words should, must, have to, or can't.
3. There is nothing that you have to do. Life is a series of choices that we make based on what we think will help us gain the things we want and avoid the things we don't want.

4. Circular questioning is the act of asking a series of questions over and over without any real attempt to answer them. The questions typically begin with why or how.

5. Magnification exaggerates an event into something bigger or worse than it actually is. Minimization or discounting describes the diminishing or belittling of positive aspects about yourself or things connected with you.

6. Negative anticipation or "what-if" thinking is characterized by imagining a host of frightening possibilities.

7. Emotional reasoning is when you use emotion rather than past experience to evaluate the possibility of something happening. When a thought triggers strong negative emotions, it is believed to be true.

8. Distorted thinking plays an important role in the development of symptoms and helps to maintain symptoms by reinforcing negative beliefs and associations from childhood.

9. Learning to identify and effectively challenge distorted thinking is one of the keys to long-term recovery.

Recommended Activities

Continue Developing Skills with the "Basics"

Chapter 6 presented four basic skills for managing anxiety. If you have not yet done the exercises at the end of that chapter, do them now before you go on. If you have been working on them but feel that you are not using them effectively, take a few days to review chapter 6 and make sure you are using each skill properly.

Begin to Identify and Challenge Your Distorted Thinking

For ten or fifteen minutes each day, think about events that have upset you. These could be situations that caused anxiety, anger, or sadness. Record as much of what you were saying to yourself during these events as you can recall. After you've recorded your self-talk, identify any forms of distorted thinking that were used. If you have difficulty remembering what you were thinking, ask yourself, "Why was this situation so important to me?" This question usually triggers thoughts about yourself and the situation. Write these thoughts down.

Next, create a rational challenge for each example of distorted thinking you identify and record it in your journal. Be sure to include a challenge for any core belief that is implied by what you said or thought. Keep in mind that some of your thoughts will probably be rational responses. Others will reflect problems that need to be worked out. Robert recorded the following self-talk that was triggered by a friend's request to go out to eat:

> I can't do this. I hate it when I'm asked to do something I don't want to do. Why does this have to happen to me now? I know I'm not going to be able to handle this. I'll go and gag on something and make a complete fool of myself.

Notice that the statement "I hate it when I'm asked to do something I don't want to do" is a simple statement of fact. No challenge is required for this. Furthermore, the request from Robert's friend is a simple problem that can be stated as "Do I accept or refuse the request?" Here is Robert's rational challenge:

> Boy, here I go again. I know that I'm not ready to eat in restaurants yet. If I choose to go, I can always say I'm not hungry and order a soda. I know I can drink without any problem. As for not liking these types of requests, this is just a statement of fact. I also know that my reaction is due to the fact that it reminds me of the difficulty I'm having with eating. The negative images of my gagging and being embarrassed are simple fortune-telling. I can

make choices that will prevent this from happening. Part of what's driving these images are the old childhood memories of being ridiculed. I'm an adult now and these people are different from the kids who used to tease me.

Review this chapter at least two times, paying close attention to the examples. Reviewing the genogram and list of core beliefs you developed while working in chapters 2 and 4 will help you develop stronger rational challenges.

Identify Distorted Thinking in the People You Know

A simple assignment that Mary, Robert, and Kimberly all found very useful was to spend a week identifying distorted thinking used by the people in their lives. You will notice more distorted thinking when people are experiencing strong emotions, tired, stressed or ill.

The purpose of this assignment is twofold: first, you will gain skill in identifying the different forms of distorted thinking discussed in this chapter. This, in turn, helps you become more aware when you are using distorted thinking. Second, you will see that distorted thinking is part of how everyone things. Keep this second point in mind as you begin to notice your own distorted thinking. Everyone uses distorted thinking from time to time. This occurs most frequently when you are experiencing strong emotions. It's easier to be logical when you are calm and feeling well. While the goal of this book is to help you reduce the occurrence of your distorted thinking, you will never eliminate all of it. Distorted thinking is just another normal aspect of being human.

During the week that you do this exercise, take a few minutes in the morning to review the various types of distorted thinking discussed in this chapter. Then, while you talk with others, watch television, listen to people talking on the radio, or listen to people talking around you, identify the various types of distorted thinking you hear. Make a game out of it, but do not tell others what you are doing. Many people become defensive or offended when their distorted thinking is pointed out. Here is a list of the five general types of distorted thinking discussed in this chapter along with the most common forms that each type takes:

Should/Must Thinking
> Characterized by words like *should, must, have to,* or *can't.*

Circular Why Questioning
> Characterized by words like *why* or *how*

Magnification/Minimization (Also called catastrophizing and discounting)

> The exaggeration of how bad some event might be

Negative Anticipation (What-if Thinking)
> Characterized by imagining a host of frightening possibilities

Emotional Reasoning
> A person tends to believe thoughts that trigger strong emotions when there is no evidence to support this belief

As you do this exercise, you may find that some of the people you know use a lot of distorted thinking. In fact, their distorted thinking may be something that causes problems in your relationships with them. If this is the case, realize that you probably won't be able to change the way they think. Instead, focus on your response to their distorted thinking. The problem of dealing with difficult people is discussed in later chapters in relation to the topics of healthy boundaries and D.E.R. scripts.

CHAPTER 8

Progressive Desensitization

I n chapter 3 we discussed how a neutral stimulus can trigger a conditioned response and how desensitization is the process of becoming unresponsive to that stimulus. This chapter describes how to desensitize in a gradual, step-by-step manner called progressive desensitization. "Progressive" refers to the fact that you begin with situations that trigger the lowest levels of anxiety and slowly work up, or progress, to those situations that trigger the highest levels of anxiety.

Developing a Plan

The key to success with desensitization is having a well thought out approach that is applied in an orderly manner. Mary presents a good example of how this is done. We first made a list of those types of situations that triggered anxiety for her and rated them from 1 to 10 according to how much anxiety each one produced and how often Mary avoided the situation. The scales we used and the list Mary developed are shown below.

Level of Anxiety

0   1   2   3   4   5   6   7   8   9   10

No Anxiety   Extreme Panic

Level of Avoidance

| 0 | 1 | 2 | 3 | 4 | 5 | 6 | 7 | 8 | 9 | 10 |

No Avoidance   Avoid Approximately   Always Avoid
50 percent of the time

Mary's Problem Situations

Situation	Level of Anxiety	Level of Avoidance
Running within 4 miles of home	2	0
Running 4-10 miles from home	4-5	3
Running on the mountain near my home	8	10
Running any course more than 10 miles from home	10	10
Being in crowds with someone I know	6	8
Being in crowds by myself	8	9
Dining out with someone I know	6	6
Dining out alone	8	9
Going to the theater alone or with someone I know	8	10
Driving out of town alone or with someone I know	10	10

Once the list was developed, the next step was to select a specific goal. Progressive desensitization is most effective when the first goal is something that produces a relatively low level of anxiety and has some practical benefit. This helps to ensure success and provides you with motivation to do the sometimes tedious work involved in desensitizing yourself.

In Mary's case, she loved to run and wanted to resume running old courses that she quit using when her anxiety became too intense. Since running close to home presented no problem for her, we developed a series of routes that were progressively farther from her home. These were areas where she had run before and where she wanted to be able to run again. We labeled them Course 1, Course 2, and Course 3. The final course took her on a path that went slightly up a mountain where she used to train but which now provoked too much anxiety.

After developing specific practice goals, I had Mary close her eyes and think about running on these practice courses. I then had her describe all of the physical sensations that she feared may occur along with all of the fearful thoughts that would be triggered by these situations. This is what she reported:

Fearful Body Sensations
Rapid heartbeat
Sweating
Light headedness
Faintness
Fatigue
"Gasping for air"

Fearful Thoughts
Something's wrong with me.
I'm going to faint.
I'm going to have a heart attack.
What if someone sees me like this?
What if I can't get help?
I'm going to die here all alone.

The next step was to develop a coping self-statement for each of the above frightening sensations and thoughts. Mary reworked her coping self-statement index cards and came up with the following. The first addressed the body sensations she feared. The second addressed her fearful thoughts.

There is nothing wrong with me. My doctor says I'm as healthy as a horse. When I run, my heart is supposed to beat fast. I'm supposed to sweat and get winded when I push hard. Afterward, I'm supposed to be fatigued. These are not signs of a problem. They are things I've experienced ever since I began to run. They are normal and safe. They are simply signs that my body is functioning the way it is supposed to function. My fears about them in the past were lies I believed because I didn't understand what had happened to me on the airplane flight during the storm.

I've never fainted even though I've feared this for a long time. I've simply hyperventilated and thought I was going to faint. Likewise, my heart is healthy.

As far as people noticing that I'm anxious, I'm an expert at being cool on the outside even when I'm panicked on the inside. Besides, most people are too into themselves to notice anything much about a stranger. Even if they do notice something, they usually don't pay much attention to it one way or the other.

I've never needed help, so based on the past, it is very unlikely that I'll need help. If I do, I have my cell phone and can easily use the speed-dial for help.

As far as dying alone goes, this is really a stretch. However, if this were to occur, it would probably happen fast and I wouldn't be worrying about it anymore. Why worry about something that is very unlikely and over which you have no control?

Basic Guidelines for Practicing

Before beginning, you should understand the basic principles of practicing. Here is the list I use:

Practice Regularly

The goal of practicing is twofold: First, you need to expose yourself to anxiety-producing triggers enough times so that you become desensitized and no longer react to them or only react mildly. Second, your goal is to convince yourself that you can face these fearful situations and continue to function and manage your anxiety effectively no matter how you feel. The only way to do this is through regular practice.

There are times when illness, work, or other problems will interfere with your practice. However, do not wait until you "feel up to it" to practice. If you had a life-threatening disease, taking medication essential for recovery would be one of your highest priorities. Practice will allow you to desensitize if it is done systematically and regularly. When thoughts such as "Why do I have to do this" or "This is so hard" come up, remind yourself of the benefits you will enjoy once your goal is accomplished. These include both the freedom to do what you want and feeling better about yourself.

A good general rule is to practice for at least an hour three times a week, daily if possible. You cannot practice too much. Practice regularly, as much as you can, for as long as you can.

Repetition Is the Key to Success

Always practice a particular situation several times before moving onto the next goal. Just because you did it once with a low level of anxiety does not mean that you are desensitized to it. You'll want to practice a given situation several times so you will have experienced it during times when you are feeling relatively calm as well as when you are feeling some anxiety. Only then will you be fully convinced that you have mastered that situation and can function regardless of how you are feeling.

Learn to Tolerate Distress

Your goal is to convince yourself that anxiety is something you can tolerate. Remember that although extreme anxiety and panic are uncomfortable, they cannot hurt you. They will not harm your body or cause any kind of insanity. You have probably already experienced the worst anxiety you will ever experience and no physical harm came to you. Although it was frightening, it did not cause any physical harm.

Remember That Anxiety Is Normal

Anxiety always accompanies new activities, so expect some anxiety to occur whenever you start a new practice goal. Remember that some of what you are experiencing is the excitement you experience whenever you challenge yourself. In other words, you may simply be mislabeling excitement as anxiety!

Expect Progress to Be Three Steps Forward and One Step Backward

A simple fact of life is that on some days you feel better than on others. Often this is simply due to being tired or ill or to the presence of several normal life stressors that happen to be occurring together. Sometimes it is not clear why it happens. However, you will occasionally slip back into old behaviors and find that situations you thought you had conquered still trigger some anxiety. This is a normal and natural part of the learning process.

Practice with as Many Factors in Your Favor as Possible

When practicing a new activity, try to keep as many factors as possible—such as time of day, size of crowd, etc.—in your favor. Once a situation is mastered with everything in your favor, you can begin practicing during times when it is more difficult.

Use Your Coping Skills at the First Sign of Anxiety

Do not "save" your skills for times when you are feeling panicky. Remember that they are most effective when used at the first sign of anxiety.

Keep Pushing Yourself a Little Bit Further

Your goal is to practice in situations that produce a low-level of anxiety, level 3 -5 on the scale at the beginning of the chapter. If your anxiety has reduced to 1 or 2 and you have practiced a particular goal several times, advance to the next step. Do not wait until you are completely at ease with a specific situation before you move on.

If you are not quite ready to proceed to the next goal but find you easily accomplish a practice session, either extend the time you spend on the activity or do just a little more than you had planned. At the same time, if you are panicky, reexamine your desensitization goal and break it into smaller, easier steps.

Remember That Desensitization Is a Trial-and-Error Process

There is no way to know before you begin how rapidly you should proceed through your desensitization goals. Identifying the most realistic desensitization goals at any given time is the result of trial and error. You discover what is "too much" by doing too much.

This will occur from time to time. When it does, it simply means that your goal needs to be broken down into two or more steps.

Examples

Usually, I like to have a person master some of the cognitive self-talk skills discussed in the last chapter before beginning desensitization. However, because Robert's symptoms were causing major interference with his daily life, we focused on basic coping strategies and began setting up desensitization goals during our second and third sessions.

Our first goal was to reduce the intensity of the panic attacks Robert was experiencing at work. Robert did not want to take medication so we decided to see what we could accomplish with the four basic skills described in chapter 6. During my first session, I always ask about a person's quality of sleep. Robert was not sleeping well. He had difficulty falling asleep and would sometimes wake up and find it difficult to get back to sleep. Whenever I hear this from someone, I immediately set quality sleep as a first goal.

Lack of sleep greatly reduces your body's ability to tolerate stress and your mind's ability to think clearly, both of which tend to increase all of the symptoms you're experiencing. If a person can sleep better, there is usually a marked improvement in all areas of life. The body is able to make routine repairs, providing more mental and physical resources for coping with anxiety. The first step in helping Robert improve the quality of his sleep was to go over the guidelines listed in Recommended Activities at the end of chapter 3 for people who are sleeping poorly. I then instructed him to use the relaxation response program when he was ready to go to sleep (see appendix 4 for more information on this).

While Robert was very restricted in what he could eat, he was working with his doctor to ensure that he received properly nourishment. At the same time, he was experiencing so much anxiety at work that he was isolating himself in his office and making every excuse he could think of to avoid coming into contact with others. While no one had said anything to him yet, there was the real possibility that this could soon become an issue with his superiors. Therefore, we decided that his greatest immediate need was to reduce the symptoms he was experiencing at work. Here are the situations Robert identified as troublesome:

Robert's Problem Situations

Situation	Level of Anxiety	Level of Avoidance
Walking outside my office door 20 feet to speak with my secretary	4	3
Walking around the unit outside of my door	5	3
Walking into another unit	5	4
Walking into the production area	6	4
Going into the conference room when no one is there	6	4
Going into the conference room for a weekly meeting	8	5
Going into the conference room for a special meeting	8	5
Talking with my supervisor	8	6
Talking with the employees under me	3	1
Going into the company cafeteria	8	8
Going into the company lounge	8	10

It is important to start with realistic expectations. We quickly realized that there was no immediate need for Robert to be able to go to the cafeteria and there was no practical way to set up a progressive desensitization schedule for meetings, two situations that triggered very high levels of anxiety and panic. On the other hand, Robert was fairly comfortable speaking with employees who were not his superiors, and he could practice being in his immediate work area without being obvious about what he was doing. Therefore, we selected the following initial goals:

1. Walking outside my office to speak with my secretary (instead of using the intercom)
2. Walking outside my office to speak to my immediate subordinates (instead of having my secretary relay my instructions)
3. Walking down the hall to the conference room and sitting in it when no one is there
4. Walking into the production area

The symptoms that Robert feared when he imagined himself doing the above were the same as those listed by Mary with one additional fearful thought that was especially strong: "What if I have a panic attack?" We addressed this fear using what I call the four-step approach to "what ifs" described in the previous chapter. Here is a summary of Robert's answers after we discussed each one at length:

How Likely Is It That I Will Have a Panic Attack?

Based on the past few weeks, there is probably only a 10 percent chance that I'll have a full-blown panic attack in the situations I've chosen to put myself in. While I often become very anxious, I usually have major attacks only in the more stressful situations. Even though I don't like it, I can handle anxiety.

How Serious Would It Be If I Had a Panic Attack?

There are no serious consequences other than being very uncomfortable. I'm not losing any money or possessions.

No physical harm is done to me or anyone I love. I'm just miserable and feeling shame and embarrassment. I'm an expert at being miserable. I've also experienced lots of shame and embarrassment. While I don't like them, I can endure them. I also know from experience that I am a real professional at appearing normal even when I'm having a panic attack.

What Steps Can I Take to Prevent a Panic Attack?

If I'm beginning to feel a little anxious, I can glance over my coping self-statements and the card that summarizes my basic skills before leaving my office. I can also choose to go out when it is less busy. Having something to eat periodically also helps.

What Can I Do to Cope with a Panic Attack?

First, I can take several relaxed diaphragmatic breaths and trigger my relaxation response. Next, I can repeat my coping self-statements. Then I need to find something to focus on, to externalize. If I feel I really do need to leave, I have memorized various explanations I could give to others that would allow me to excuse myself from the situation.

Robert summarized the above ideas into the following coping self-statement:

While there's the possibility that I may have a panic attack, I usually do fine in these situations. The anxiety I do experience is usually not that bad. I now have new tools for managing my symptoms and know how to get back to my safe area if I'm more uncomfortable than I want to be. I also know that there is nothing dangerous about what I'm experiencing.

Robert began taking frequent short excursions into the locations at work to which he wanted to become desensitized. He would review his notes and then spend fifteen to forty-five minutes in a specific area. He worked through each area, one at a time, until he could again go comfortably to all of the areas in his unit. As with most people who experience anxiety-related symptoms, Robert was very creative. He was able to make his excursions look like they were part of his job so others didn't realize what he was doing.

Increased Suggestibility

People with severe anxiety often are more suggestible to negative ideas, especially those that are associated with their anxiety. This heightened suggestibility can intensify the various types of negative and catastrophic thinking discussed in the previous chapter and become a major force that interferes with desensitization and promotes a state of excessive anxiety.

Suggestibility is the acceptance of an idea without analyzing it critically. Suggestibility is sometimes very useful. For example, when you watch a movie, your ability to ignore the fact that you are just watching moving images and listening to recorded sounds allows you to enter into the movie as if you were actually there, experiencing what the characters were experiencing. Sometimes, though, suggestibility can be damaging, as in the case of Mary or Robert. Whenever they heard or read about problems that were sometimes associated with severe anxiety they failed to analyze what they read carefully and, instead, would immediately believe that what they read must also be true for them. As they dwelled on what they had read, their fear would generate symptoms that seemed to confirm what they had feared.

Mary, for instance, heard that suicide was sometimes associated with panic disorder. She began to worry that she might commit suicide, and within a few days this became an overwhelming obsession. While many people with panic disorder do have occasional suicidal thoughts, they are usually just passing ones, such as "I wish I were dead," and are similar to those that anyone experiencing major difficulties might have. I've worked with hundreds of people, and it has been very rare when a person with panic disorder has had serious thoughts of suicide. Once I explained this to Mary, her obsession with the idea that she might be suicidal quickly diminished. Within a couple of weeks it was gone.

Two factors cause this increased suggestibility. First, anxiety, like any intense emotion, interferes with your ability to reason. This is why the written exercises presented in this book are so important. Writing down your thoughts helps you analyze critically what you are thinking. Having written copies of your coping self-statement that you carry with you allows you to use them when you are in the middle of an activity and are finding it difficult to think of effective challenges for the negative self-talk you are using.

Increased suggestibility can result also from a childhood where the child is not allowed to disagree with the parents. Previous chapters have detailed how Mary was punished simply for disagreeing with her parents. Robert's parents were so terrifying that he dared not say, do, or think anything that might upset them. As a result, both Mary and Robert began simply to accept whatever their parents said as true, whether it seemed logical or not. In essence, being overly suggestible was reinforced until it became automatic. To use an extreme example, if an abusive parent says, "The sky is green," a child has to make it so and ignore his or her own reason and senses. To do otherwise is to risk the pain of abandonment or punishment.

One way to be less suggestible is to take time to evaluate things that you hear or read. This is especially important in our digital age where so much misinformation is presented as reliable.

Whenever you become anxious about something, it's a message that you need to use the step-by-step methods you are learning in this book to evaluate your thinking. It is especially helpful to write things down so you can view your worries more objectively. As these skills become more and more automatic, your suggestibility will decrease. Of course, as your overall level of anxiety decreases, you will also find it easier to use your logic. A second way to be less suggestible is learning to trust your judgement. This will be discussed in more detail in the chapters that follow.

Summary of Key Ideas

1. Desensitization is the process of becoming unresponsive to a stimulus that formerly triggered a conditioned response. Progressive desensitization is the application of this process in a "progressive" manner, starting with situations that trigger the lowest levels of anxiety and slowly working up, or progressing, to those that trigger the highest levels of anxiety.

2. The first step in progressive desensitization is to make a list of situations that trigger anxiety and rate each one according to (1) how much anxiety each one produces and (2) how often you avoid each situation.

3. The second step is to select a specific practice goal and begin practicing regularly. Your first goal needs to be a situation or place that produces a relatively low level of anxiety. It helps to choose a goal has some practical benefit.

4. The third step to complete prior to beginning desensitization is to imagine yourself practicing and make a list of all the fearful physical sensations that might occur along with the fearful thoughts you've had while doing this activity in the past. After the list is completed,

develop coping self-statements that address each sensation and fear and write them down on index cards.

5. The fourth step is to begin practicing. Review the cards with your coping self-statements and the nine guidelines for practicing prior to each practice session until you have internalized them. If new fearful sensations or thoughts occur, develop additional coping self-statements to deal with them after your practice session.

6. Work through the four-step approach to "what ifs" whenever you have a specific worry.

7. People suffering from severe anxiety tend to be more suggestible. This is usually due to a decrease in the ability to reason caused by the anxiety. For some, childhood factors can also contribute to increased suggestibility. Take time to evaluate things you read and are told to see if they are really true.

Recommended Activities

Make a List of Problem Situations

Follow the examples given in this chapter to create a list of situations that trigger anxiety. Rate each one using the two scales given at the beginning of the chapter. Next, select a specific desensitization goal. Keep in mind that this needs to be something that only triggers a moderate to low level of anxiety. It also helps to choose a goal that has some practical benefit.

Develop Specialized Coping Self-Statements

Take a moment to think about being in the situation you have chosen for your desensitization practice. Make a list of all the frightening body sensations you think you might feel. Then make a list of the types of frightening thoughts triggered by this situation.

Once you've compiled your lists, develop a coping self-statement that addresses each item on the lists. When developing coping self-statements for fearful possibilities, be sure you work through the four-step approach to "what ifs."

Begin Desensitizing

After you have completed the first two recommended activities, choose times when you will actually begin your desensitization work. During the first two weeks, be sure to review the practice guidelines and your coping self-statements before each practice session. After this, you probably need to review the guidelines only once a week.

Carry your notes and coping cards with you so you can refer to them while you practice. Continue to do this until these skills become an immediate and automatic response to anxiety.

Use Your Journal to Begin Hearing the Message of Anxiety

Continue to record times when you are upset in your journal. Follow the guidelines given in chapter 7 for identifying and challenging any distorted thinking you identify. You can also use your journal to record how your practice sessions go and work out new coping self-statements whenever a new frightening thought or body sensation occurs.

On days when practicing is more difficult than usual, take a few minutes to record all of the stresses—physical (sick, hungry, tired), mental, relationship, and spiritual—you are experiencing. After several weeks you may see important patterns and identify stresses that increase your symptoms. When this happens, it is usually a message that you need to develop more effective ways of dealing with the problem stress you've identified.

Use the Four-Step Approach to Analyze Your Worries

Take time to record your worries in your journal and analyze them using the four-step approach for dealing with "what ifs" discussed in both the this chapter and the previous one.. Record your conclusions. This will allow you to refer back to your work when these fears resurface. If you're working with a recurring worry, create a coping self-statement and write it on a card that you can keep with you.

If You Are Not Getting Quality Sleep

Read appendix 3, Suggestions for Better Sleep, and follow the guidelines given there.

CHAPTER 9

Moving from Basic to Advanced Symptom Control

Mary, Robert, and Kimberly were able to reach the level of basic symptom control relatively quickly. Indeed, once a person has a good understanding of how anxiety-related problems develop and are maintained, he or she is able to begin challenging the two main lies that maintain anxiety-related problems: (1) Something dangerous is occurring that might harm or kill me or possible cause me to lose my mind in some way, and (2) these symptoms will render me helpless or cause me to do something embarrassing or dangerous. Challenging these lies effectively usually brings about some reduction in symptoms; however, it does not eliminate conditioned-response triggers for anxiety or avoidance patterns. It is the work of desensitization that begins to quiet these triggers and move a person from basic symptom control to the next level, advanced symptom control. In addition, a person needs to develop an awareness of at least some of the core beliefs and associations that played a role in the development and maintenance of symptoms.

First Steps to Advanced Symptom Control

Movement to the second level of recovery, advanced symptom control, usually involves a process of adapting the skills presented in the previous chapters to your individual personality, history, and current life situation.

One idea that was especially difficult for Mary to accept was the fact that anxiety isn't dangerous, it's just terribly uncomfortable. This is a common problem and what helped Mary overcome it was the thought that she had already experienced the worst panic attack without suffering any physical harm from it.

To realize this, I had her recall her worst episodes of anxiety and asked how she responded to them. She realized that she was able to move and think even though she was terrified. The attacks did not harm her physically, and even though the many "what if" thoughts she had seemed very real, none of them happened. These episodes were just very frightening experiences that left her believing a host of lies about herself and what had happened.

As we identified specific lies, Mary reworked her coping self-statement cards so that they addressed them directly. Here is the card she created after our third session and which she began to use along with the one shown in chapter 6.

> My initial symptoms left me believing the lie that something was wrong with my body. The symptoms were due to hyperventilation, fear, and being very tired. My doctor confirmed that I am strong and healthy and in great shape. My heart can beat fast with no problem. Any tingling or shortness of breath is just hyperventilation. They are normal responses to fear and automatic conditioned responses. I now have skills to manage them.

Mary also found it helpful to recall the body sensations she experienced while running marathons and shorter races prior to the onset of her symptoms. This helped her realize that her fear of running was due to her mislabeling normal sensations as dangerous. Here is the card she made that addressed this issue:

It is normal to breathe heavily when running. It is also normal for my heart to beat fast. I've experienced these sensations as long as I've been running. Because they are similar to sensations I've felt when panicked, I've been mislabeling them as dangerous. They are not dangerous. They are safe and normal. My body is responding to the physical demand of running just as it is supposed to respond.

I also had her hyperventilate in my office by breathing rapidly for a minute. This caused her to experience some of the dizziness and lightheadedness she associated with panic attacks. While this made her anxious and uncomfortable, she could see that she was able to walk and think and function even though she was uncomfortable.

As a result of the above work, Mary found that within her safe area, the high level of anxiety she had been experiencing reduced to a very low level over the course of about five weeks. Although she still experienced excessive anxiety whenever she was in crowds or ventured more than ten miles from home or in other situations that were strong triggers, she was able to resume running as long as she stayed close to home. Mary had achieved the first level of recovery, basic symptom control, and was beginning to move to the second level, advanced symptom control.

While Mary could avoid strong triggers and stay in a safe area, Robert had a host of anxiety-provoking triggers at work, plus the primary trigger, eating. As mentioned in the last chapter, this made it important for him to begin working on a program of desensitization while developing the basic symptom-reducing skills. Robert's symptoms did not quiet down as quickly as Mary's, but, by the end of the third week, they had decreased enough so that he was able to function again in a fairly normal manner in the area around his office.

One of the greatest stumbling blocks for Robert was his tendency to think that people were watching him closely, noticing his anxiety, and thinking poorly of him. Often, he would imagine that people were talking about him and making jokes about his problem behind his back. Sometimes he would even imagine himself being fired.

It was clear that Robert's childhood fears and memories were fueling his unrealistic, but fearful thoughts. When I asked him for an objective evaluation of his immediate staff, Robert reported that they were actually very nice, supportive people. Robert recalled a time about a year earlier when the child of one of the staff members had a severe illness. During that time, the whole department rallied around that staff member and was very thoughtful. Robert also recalled how the conversations held behind this person's back were sympathetic ones. As a result of this, he developed the following coping self-statement card:

> While I may be anxious, there is nothing wrong with me physically or mentally. My anxiety is just a holdover from all of the lies I've been telling myself and the many conditioned-response triggers I've developed.

> I can talk and do my job even when I'm anxious. I've been doing this for quite some time now. No one pays that much attention to my anxiety. Most probably don't even notice it or they think that it's just the way I am. They're too busy with work and their own problems to pay much attention to what I'm thinking or doing.

> Even if someone notices, they all know the pressure I've been under to complete this project. They usually just attribute symptoms in others as due to stress. They will do the same with me.

My secretary is very supportive and sympathetic. She does not think badly of me.

Just take things slowly. Do as much and go as far as you can. People are too wrapped up in their own business to pay much attention to me.

Here is an additional card Robert made that addressed the time-tunnel aspect of his excessive concern with what others might think about him:

The feelings I have about people thinking poorly of me are just holdovers from childhood—I'm time-tunneling. My parents belittled me and I was bullied at school. These people are not my parents or the bullies at school. They are co-workers and subordinates. I'm no longer a child. I'm a supervisor and an adult.

Many of these people respond to me as an authority figure. I have power and choices I didn't have as a child.

Confronting Death and Uncertainty

Kimberly used the same basic tools and cognitive-behavioral approach as Mary and Robert. However, because her symptoms were due to posttraumatic stress disorder, the issues she needed to address were different. It turned out that Kimberly had three key issues to work through. The first was the fact that she was now much more aware of her mortality and inability to control many of the circumstances in her life.

One of the ways we cope with danger is simply to ignore it. Once you have a life-threatening experience, you can no longer ignore the potential for danger, at least in similar situations. This is one of the main reasons we become more cautious as we get older. Young people haven't had as many encounters with danger as older people have. It's easy for them to ignore the dangers of driving fast or doing other potentially harmful activities. As you mature, you experience harm firsthand or see friends and loved ones experience harm in various situations. This gives a reality to danger and to our inability to control many events that were not present when young.

Over time, we also become increasingly aware of the fact that we are mortal and will die someday. Young people tend to act and think as if they will live forever. As you age, more aches and pains develop and you begin to notice your body losing the resiliency of youth. You also begin to experience the death of people you know. This last event frequently is a shock. In times past, people saw death in others due to childhood diseases, injuries, infections, and genetic defects from a young age. In our modern world, many people don't experience the death of a friend or loved is one until they are adults. Indeed, the death of a close friend or loved one is one of the factors that triggered the onset of severe anxiety in some of the clients I've seen.

In Kimberly's case, she had a life-threatening experience. This ordeal was the result of another person's actions; it was unpredictable, and it definitely was dangerous. Prior to this, she thought she could handle anything, and that nothing serious could happen to her. The assault shattered that belief. The fact that several people had been injured in her district that year became much more real to her. Kimberly came to therapy thinking that once she "got over" her problem, she would be able to return to her old way of thinking and dealing with life. This was an unrealistic expectation.

Because Kimberly had to rethink her beliefs about death and her physical limitations, this became a recurring topic during our sessions. Initially, Kimberly was faced with the choice of either deciding to transfer to a position that was less dangerous or to adjust to the idea that she would have to be more aware and cautious in the future. As we focused on this reality, Kimberly began to realize how much she was beating herself up for being "weak." She did this because of two childhood beliefs: "Mistakes are not acceptable" and "I must be strong and never show weakness."

Challenging these erroneous core beliefs became the second major area of work for Kimberly. She found the idea that she was "a normal person who was in an abnormal situation" especially helpful. This, along with the knowledge of how the mind reacts to trauma presented in chapter 3, helped her understand that her mind needed time to process the assault. The fact that anyone traumatized severely enough would have similar symptoms helped her begin to think of herself as normal. She especially liked the idea that flashbacks were simply "snapshots" that the mind was looking at, one at a time, in order to "process" the event.

Also important to Kimberly's therapy was her understanding of the conditioned-response nature of her reaction. She had spent her life thinking that she could "will" herself to do anything and respond however she wanted to respond. This was the first time she realized that there were some situations where willpower simply didn't work. By becoming alarmed when she could not "will" away the conditioned-response anxiety triggered by people or situations similar to those present during the assault, she was actually increasing her symptoms. Kimberly loved the relaxation-response recording I gave her and was amazed at how well she responded to it. This response not only gave her needed relief from her symptoms but also helped her see how strong and automatic conditioned responses can be.

Here is the card that Kimberly developed that incorporated these various ideas:

> I used to think I was indestructible and that nothing serious would ever happen to me. The assault has opened my eyes to the fact that this is not true. This does not make me a wimp or somehow less of a person. It only

means I'm more experienced in life and will assess dangers more realistically.

Any person traumatized like I was will experience posttraumatic stress disorder symptoms.

I'm a normal person who has experienced an abnormal situation. Because of this, I'm having normal reactions to something that was too much for me to handle all at once.

The anxiety and flashbacks I sometimes experience are not a sign of being weak-willed. Conditioned responses can occur no matter how strong-willed you are. Quit beating yourself up and use your skills. You have already seen them work and you will desensitize over time.

During the first month, Kimberly continued to experience regular flashbacks and excessive anxiety whenever she encountered something that reminded her of the assault. However, her symptoms reduced greatly during normal activities, and she began to regain confidence in herself.

Shame

Another factor that can keep a person stuck at the first level of recovery and focused on symptoms is shame. Shame is usually defined as a painful emotion caused by a strong sense of guilt, embarrassment, unworthiness, or disgrace. Within the model of emotions presented in chapter 4, shame is due to a sense of loss, and, therefore, a type of sadness. The loss that triggers shame is the perceived loss of one's reputation or the diminishing of one's self-image. In essence, shame comes from the perception that one has been "stained" or damaged in some irreparable way. This can be due to an event such as a rape or childhood molestation or to a core belief that causes the perception that one is inferior to others in some significant way. Often, as with Mary, Robert, and Kimberly, shame is triggered by both types of loss. For example, the assault that triggered Kimberly's posttraumatic stress disorder was not only a stain on her reputation but also evidence that she didn't measure up to the unrealistic expectation that she "should" be able to handle anything. In Mary's and Robert's case, their panic disorder both confirmed the core belief from childhood that they were inadequate and did not measure up to others and served as a lasting "mark" of that inadequacy that everyone could see.

One of the keys to long-term recovery is realizing that everyone has weaknesses and struggles. They are just a normal part of the human condition. If you have a sensitive body or have experienced something extraordinary, it is normal to experience the symptoms of anxiety. This "normalizing" of oneself is also the key to overcoming the sense of shame that goes along with not only anxiety-related problems but a host of problems that people face. As Mary, Robert, and Kimberly slowly came to redefine what it meant to be human and what was normal, they found their sense of shame gradually lifted. As you will read in the chapters that follow, one of the main tasks for them in achieving this was to challenge core beliefs from childhood that either demanded impossibly high standards or that identified them as inadequate in some way.

Summary of Key Ideas Presented in this Chapter

1. The basic skills presented in chapters 5 through 8 need to be adapted to your individual personality, history, and life situation.

2. While basic symptom control is achieved fairly quickly, it usually takes several weeks or months to move to advanced symptom control. Be patient.

3. A person usually needs to overcome several stumbling blocks in order to achieve advanced symptom control. These vary widely from person to person. This chapter presented the following five:

- It takes time to become convinced that anxiety isn't dangerous.
- The childhood message "I don't measure up" can cause the belief that others think poorly of you.
- It's often difficult to come to terms with our mortality and inability to control many of life's circumstances.
- The unconscious conditioned responses associated with severe anxiety means that your initial goal is to manage anxiety rather than eliminate it. Managing anxiety to you can be anxious and still do the things you want to do is the key to desensitization, which leads to symptom reduction.
- It takes time to replace deep-seated lies with the truth.

4. Shame is a painful emotion caused by a strong sense of being tainted or damaged in some way that causes a sense of loss, and, therefore, a type of sadness.

5. The key to overcoming shame is to redefine what it means to be human and challenge core beliefs from childhood that either demanded impossibly high standards or that identify you as inadequate in some way. This is a part of learning to see yourself as normal.

Recommended Activities

Identify Your Key Stumbling Blocks and Develop Coping Self-Statements That Address Them

In the previous chapters, you identified core beliefs and associations that played a role in the development and maintenance of your symptoms. Use the models presented in this chapter to develop a card that addresses each issue you've identified. Review this card daily for at least two weeks. If you have not yet identified core beliefs and associations that play a role in your symptoms, review chapter 4 and do the Recommended Activities it suggests.

Repetition, Repetition, Repetition

As you read through these case examples, keep in mind that the work described in this chapter covered a period of many weeks. Mary's acceptance that anxiety was not dangerous, for example, did not come about as the result of one session. As she practiced desensitization, and we together worked on other issues, we would periodically go over the information presented at the beginning of this chapter. Mary would leave the session confident that anxiety was not dangerous. However, after a short time, sometimes only a few hours, the old fears would wash over her and drown out this truth. As we went over the ideas in subsequent sessions, and she began to use coping self-statements that addressed this issue directly, she slowly became convinced that it was true.

When you have believed a lie and repeated it to yourself over and over, it takes time to be convinced of the truth. In order for the truth to become a conviction that is stronger than the lies you've been telling yourself, you may need to reread the sections of this book that address the specific lies that drive your anxiety several times.

If you had a difficult childhood, many of the defenses you developed to cope with childhood problems may be interfering with your ability to look at yourself objectively. When this is the case, it takes much repetition and persistence to penetrate these defenses.

Use Your Journal to Challenge Problem Core Beliefs and Associations

It is now time to begin putting together the different pieces of the previous chapters. If you have not yet begun to write in a journal for at least fifteen minutes every other day, review the suggestions given in the "Recommended Activities" section of chapters 3, 5, and 8.

As you record your self-talk when you are upset, identify the underlying beliefs or associations supporting the distorted thinking that is contributing to your actions and thoughts. These will usually be the core beliefs and associations you identified while doing the recommended activities in chapter 4. If you have not done them, go back and do them now.

In essence, you are now working at two different levels. The first is simply to develop logical challenges for the various forms of distorted thinking you use as was described in chapter 7. The second is to identify the underlying beliefs and associations upon which the surface self-talk is based, as described in this chapter. While this second task is more difficult, once you become skilled at it, you will find it a powerful tool for changing how you respond to events.

If you're finding it difficult to identify and challenge core beliefs and associations, you may need someone to help you. This person could be a friend, a relative, a fellow sufferer whom you trust, a pastor or a professional therapist. Remember that it is usually easier to see others objectively than it is to see yourself.

Continue Desensitization

If you have avoidance patterns or situations that provoke severe anxiety, continue practicing systematic desensitization as discussed in the last chapter. Keep in mind that you need to repeat a given practice activity many times before you move on to a new goal.

Also, keep in mind the conditioned-response nature of much of your anxiety. Understanding why your anxiety is triggered will not stop a given situation from activating it. Only time and continued, systematic practice will do that. Your goal is to convince yourself that you can function in a given situation, even when you're anxious.

CHAPTER 10

Establishing Healthy Boundaries

O ne of the drawbacks in writing a book like this one is the need to summarize in a few pages work that often takes weeks or months to accomplish. This can give the impression that someone comes to a session, gains an important insight or learns a new skill, then lives happily ever after. If only it was that easy! Achieving long-term recovery actually takes many months depending on how many issues are intertwined with the anxiety symptoms and whether or not you are using an effective approach.

Complex learning is always accomplished through a series of steps over time. Consider how long it takes to learn to read and write. Even when an adult is learning this skill, it usually takes several months for him or her to be able to read comfortably at a sixth-grade level. Compared to changing complex habit patterns that have been ingrained for many years, learning to read is easy!

What Are Boundaries in Human Relationships?

When applied to human relationships, a boundary refers to the limits we place on relationships. As we grow and develop, we learn to set limits on how much of ourselves we disclose to others, to what extent we allow others to influence us, what we are willing to do for others and what we allow others to do to us. These limits can be thought of as our personal boundaries.

The person with weak boundaries is like a piece of property with little or no fencing. People can come and go as they please and take or leave whatever they want. The person with rigid boundaries is like a piece of property with high, thick walls and no gates. Nothing gets in, and nothing gets out. In contrast, a person with healthy boundaries is like a piece of property with a strong wall and a gate that can be easily opened or closed by the owner depending upon who is approaching and what the approaching person wants. The gate is opened to receive people who have proven themselves trustworthy and whose requests seem reasonable. Similarly, it is closed when people approaching are hurtful or are making inappropriate requests.

In order to have healthy boundaries you need to be able to:

- Recognize when your boundaries are being ignored by others;
- Identify what you can do to establish healthy boundaries in a given situation; and
- Use assertive skills to enforce your boundaries.

Missing Anxiety's Message

The concept of boundaries takes us back to one of the central themes of this book: that anxiety is a message. Unfortunately, when ignored for years, messages about boundary violations can become difficult to recognize. Mary presents a good example of this.

After several months of therapy, Mary's symptoms had reduced considerably and she was able to do many of the things that had been difficult when she first came to me. She was moving from basic symptom control to a high level of advanced symptom control. Since much of the work at this stage is in the area of systematic desensitization and applying the skills presented in the previous chapters to everyday situations, we were now only meeting every three weeks. During one session Mary came in and reported that after doing well for several weeks, her symptoms had begun to increase and she was finding it difficult to practice. I asked her if anything unusual had happened. She reported that everything in her life was just as it had been before.

Things often seem to be going well for someone when, all of a sudden, symptoms seem to escalate for no apparent reason. Closer examination usually reveals a logical explanation. In order to understand the increase in Mary's symptoms, I asked her to give me a detailed account of daily events starting just before her symptoms began to increase. In describing the previous week, she mentioned in passing, "My mother's birthday is in two weeks, and my brother called to arrange a family get-together."

Because Mary had described so much pain associated with her family, this simple statement was a giant red flag. Indeed, as we began to discuss this upcoming get-together, Mary realized that she was very anxious about it. It had been some time since she had seen her family all together. Furthermore, she began to recall how abusively she had been treated at past gatherings. As the cause of the increase in Mary's anxiety became clear, she was puzzled as to why she had missed it.

As a child, Mary viewed her parents' inappropriate behavior as normal since it was all she had known. Since there was nothing she could do to stop her family's abusive treatment, she learned to become numb to it. Ignoring the rejection and emotional pain associated with her mother also allowed Mary to obtain the small amount of positive attention that her mother was able to give her. Ignoring was also the way in which both Mary's father and mother dealt with difficult emotional issues. Thus, the rule "don't look, don't feel, run away" can be seen as something that Mary learned not only out of necessity but by example.

Mary's perception of her family's abusive behavior as normal, and her ability to bury the hurt associated with her family had become so automatic that she had immediately pushed out of consciousness the fact that the upcoming time with her mother would be painful. However, the pain connected with her mother and past experiences where she was helpless to protect herself from her family were realities that, on an unconscious level, could not be ignored. The result was increased anxiety as her fight-or-flight response was triggered.

Once Mary became aware of the message her anxiety was sending–that she was fearful of being treated poorly at the family gathering–she needed to decide what she was going to do about the upcoming event. Did she want to participate in an event that would be painful, or did she want to stay home? If she decided to attend, she needed to develop a plan for coping with the hurtful behavior of her family—a plan for enforcing her personal boundaries.

If you have important issues from childhood that you learned to ignore or label as normal, you probably have times when your symptoms seem to increase for no apparent reason. When this occurs, take a moment to see if there are any significant family-related events or commemorative dates, such as birthdays or anniversaries, coming up. If so, it may be that the upcoming event or date has triggered anxiety-related to family issues.

Mary's Plan

Mary's family had a long history of ignoring her boundaries. This was especially true of her mother, who was very critical, asked inappropriate personal questions, and frequently made inappropriate requests. As we discussed this, Mary decided that the most hurtful behaviors during the gathering would likely be the result of her mother's drinking. Her mother's usual pattern was to begin drinking just before dinner, continue drinking after dinner, and become increasingly verbally abusive as the evening wore on. As the rest of the family began drinking, they would become abusive toward one another, especially toward Mary.

At this point Mary decided that she really did want to see her family. Even though she is an intelligent woman with good judgment, she wasn't sure how she could protect herself from their painful behavior. The reason for her difficulty was the childhood message "I'm not as intelligent or capable as others and can't do anything correctly," which caused her to doubt her ability to figure things out and come up with good solutions. Since people who find it difficult to think clearly about their own problems often have the ability to see the problems of others objectively, I asked Mary, "What would you tell a friend who was having this problem?"

Mary decided that her "friend" needed to get an inexpensive motel room so she could leave right after dinner before her mother started to become abusive. I then said, "That sounds like it might also work for you." At first, Mary found it difficult to see how a solution that would be appropriate for a friend would be appropriate for her. After a little thought and discussion, she began to see how this idea was exactly what she needed to do.

Next, we discussed ways in which Mary could protect herself while she was around her family. Since she was not yet feeling strong enough to confront her mother directly, she developed several socially acceptable excuses for leaving when things became too uncomfortable. In addition, Mary and I developed several strategies for changing the subject in case a topic came up that prompted criticism from her parents or brothers.

In the weeks that followed, whenever Mary described a situation in which she was confused as to what an appropriate boundary should be, as a starting point I asked her what she would tell a friend with this problem. After doing this for several weeks, Mary found herself trusting her judgment more and more.

If you doubt your ability to respond to a difficult interpersonal situation, use this same approach and pretend you are talking to a friend who has asked for your advice. Try to come up with the best possible solution. Like Mary, you will probably come up with a pretty good solution. If you find it difficult to use this approach, or to accept that your solution is a good one, consult someone who has proven to be reliable and clear thinking. See what he or she thinks of the solution you've developed. While he or she might have useful additions, you'll probably find that you have a stronger ability to develop appropriate answers yourself than you had previously believed. You just simply didn't trust your ability.

As Mary worked out a specific plan for all of the anxiety-producing situations connected with the family event she could think of, her symptoms lessened substantially. Nevertheless, her anxiety remained at a higher level than normal until the event had passed. This is normal; the event was a major challenge for Mary. After the get-together, it took two weeks for her anxiety to return to its previous level and for her to feel that she was again making substantial progress. This is also normal. The emotional stress of this event was similar to being sick with a bad cold or the flu. Mary's body was drained, and it took time for it to regain its physical and emotional strength.

One other activity Mary found helpful was to act as an observer during some of the time she spent with her family. When she simply observed her family's interaction in as objective a manner as she could, she was amazed at what she saw. The insights she gained proved very useful in the weeks to come when she challenged old beliefs about herself and her place in the world.

If you are going to be around your family, you might also find it useful to spend some time observing their behavior and interactions. Keep in mind that you are only gathering information. Pretend that you are a research scientist studying how your family members treat one another. Identify the unspoken rules and beliefs that guide your family's interactions. You'll probably be surprised at what you find. As you do this, keep your observations private as telling your family what you're doing will probably cause conflict.

Holiday Anxiety

Holiday anxiety refers to increased anxiety that is experienced from early November through the first week or two in January. For some, it can start as early as the beginning of October. Holiday anxiety is usually seen in adults raised in dysfunctional families. It's a type of conditioned response that develops because parents with limited coping skills become more abusive during the holidays. A critical parent, for example, becomes more critical, while a physically abusive parent becomes more out of control.

During childhood, holiday decorations and music become associated with the pain of increased abuse. They become signals that danger is approaching. This association triggers conditioned response anxiety during the holidays when that person is an adult. This phenomenon is so common I often tell someone who is experiencing holiday anxiety, "You'll probably feel much better around January 15th." As they begin to feel better after the holidays, many are amazed at my "predictive" ability. However, a quick review of the causes of holiday anxiety makes this prediction less remarkable. What is amazing is how blind we can be to key issues.

One way to manage holiday anxiety is to use the "what's real, what's happening" technique described in chapter 3. Here is what Mary wrote on a card after we discussed her holiday anxiety. She then read it once a day for several days until she could paraphrase it without much thinking whenever she noticed her anxiety or irritability increasing.

> What's happening: I'm experiencing a conditioned emotional response that was caused by frightening things that occurred in my home during the holidays. Mom and

dad became more abusive, and I was constantly on the alert to stay out of their way and below the radar.

What's real: I'm now away from them in my own home, and I control what happens here. I am safe and I can make the holidays into whatever I want.

In addition to using this technique, Mary took time to look at the things she did during the holidays in the past. She identified activities that were energy draining and no longer brought joy along with those that generated negative emotions. She then identified activities that she actually enjoyed and wanted to do. She also noted that, in the past, she tended to exhaust herself by doing too much. So, in addition to focusing her time on things she enjoyed, she also decided to take better care of herself and only do as much as she had the energy for. By following Mary's example, you'll find that over the course of two or three holidays you can diminish most of the holiday anxiety you experience.

Honoring Your Rights

The final step in developing appropriate boundaries is learning how to be assertive. Usually, the two biggest roadblocks for this are a poor self-image and thoughts about yourself and others that cause you to believe that you have no right to protect or assert yourself. The result is that these two roadblocks can cause a person who knows how to be assertive to find it difficult to use their assertive skills in at least some situations. Situational nonassertiveness like this usually involves situations with parents, spouses, authority figures, siblings, or close friends. It was this lack of belief in her rights that made it difficult for Mary to see that the solutions that were appropriate for her "friend" were also appropriate for her.

Even a cursory glance at Mary's background, as given in chapter 2, makes clear how she developed her sense of not having any rights. In the weeks after our initial session, Mary recalled other ways in which she was treated with disrespect while growing up. For example, when her brothers teased her or were mean, her mother would ignore the situation or tell her, "Don't make such a big deal out of things." Mary even remembered several incidents where she tried to express an opinion that differed from her mother's and was told, "You've got no right to think like that."

One of the activities Mary found helpful was to develop a list of "rights" that were difficult for her to affirm. She wrote these on a card and read them to herself two or three times a day for a month. By the end of the month, she found that it was much easier both to identify boundary violations and to take action to set appropriate limits. Here is a list of rights I use with clients:

> I have the right to be treated with dignity and respect.
> I have the right to decide what is best for me.
> I have the right to have and express my own feelings and opinions.
> I have the right to ask for what I want and need.
> I have the right to say "no" without feeling guilty.
> I have the right to be listened to and taken seriously.
> I have the right to do what is necessary to protect my physical and mental health, even though this sometimes causes discomfort to others.

The Excessive Need for Approval

Another factor that causes a person to have weak boundaries and be nonassertive is an excessive need for approval. It is normal and healthy to want others to like and approve of you. You can't have a healthy relationship unless there is some desire to please the other person. At the same time, this need can become so exaggerated that it destroys relationships and cause you to ignore your needs. An excessive need for approval usually comes from growing up in a home where the needs of a child to feel loved and important were inadequately met.

When you have an excessive need for approval, you tend to avoid doing anything that will cause disapproval. The excessive need for approval is often referred to as a fear of rejection or fear of abandonment and plays a major role in the development of weak boundaries and nonassertive behavior. Whenever you assert yourself or tell others "no," there is the possibility that they might reject you or disapprove of you. For someone with an excessive need for approval, this can be too great a risk to take.

Two common traits frequently connected with an excessive need for approval are indecision and difficulty accepting criticism. Indecision is due to the fear that a wrong decision might bring disapproval; difficulty accepting criticism results because criticism tends to be seen as rejection, even when it is given in a constructive manner.

Two additional problems that can be associated with an excessive need for approval are excessive dependency and jealousy. A person with these traits is often overly demanding of friends' or a mate's time and attention. When they see someone important to them spending time with someone else, they may become jealous because this person is "stealing" some of the attention they are so dependent upon.

Mary and Robert both had an excessive need for approval. While Mary was not troubled with jealousy, she did have a big problem with weak boundaries and being nonassertive. Robert, on the other hand, had developed fairly rigid boundaries as a means of protecting himself as a child. At the same time, he described many incidents where he was very jealous and demanding in his relationships. While Robert was able to be fairly assertive in his role as a supervisor, he was often not so with his wife and close friends. More is said about assertiveness in the next chapter.

Summary Sheets

Because you are working to change deeply ingrained beliefs and habit patterns, you will tend to forget important insights and new skills. This is normal. New knowledge and skills often need to be relearned several times before they are fully internalized. Summary sheets are an excellent method you can use to make this process easier. A summary sheet is a page that addresses one specific core belief, association, or behavior that you have identified as an underlying recurring problem.

To create a summary sheet, begin by listing the core belief, association, or behavior at the top of the page. Then create the following sections:

- Why this is an issue
- Situations where this causes problems
- Things I can tell myself
- Things I can do

Here is the summary sheet that Robert created to deal with the issue of approval:

The Excessive Need for Approval

Why This Is an Issue
My parents were so broken that they were unable to give me the love I needed as a child. They were often cold and rejecting. While I developed rigid walls to protect myself, I still desperately wanted their love.

Situations Where this Causes Problems

1. When my wife goes to a work function or off with her friends, I tend to feel abandoned and rejected by her. In the past, I became angry and would nitpick and criticize her before and after events like these.
2. When I see my wife or one of my good friends talking with someone in a social situation, I tend to barge in and dominate the conversation.
3. I often have difficulty telling my wife what I want. When we have a disagreement I tend to crawl back into my shell and stop talking.
4. I tend to react to criticism badly, whether it's a job review or simple advice from a friend. I'll either withdraw or lash out.

Things I Can Tell Myself

Rejection and disapproval are a part of life. While I don't like them and would prefer everyone to like me, I don't have to fear them. Most of the disapproval and rejection I experience has little to do with me. The other person is usually sick, hungry, tired, or angry at something or someone other than me. I also know that others often time tunnel as I do and withdraw because they are mixing up the present with their past. The bottom line is that there will always be some who won't like me no matter what I do, just as there are people I don't like. As for my friends, wife, and child, rejection is a temporary part of any healthy relationship. Sometimes the rejection I feel is really me rejecting myself or feeling down on myself.

Things I Can Do

1. The most important thing for me to do is stop and think when I begin to feel jealous or hurt. Take a

moment to ask the two time-tunnel questions "What's happening" and "What is real?"

2. When I feel jealous in a social situation, and notice myself taking over, be quiet and recall the things I can tell myself that I've written above.

3. Practice listening to others, especially when I see myself dominating a conversation.

4. When I have an argument or disagreement with my wife, take a time-out and use the assertive skills I'm learning to approach the disagreement in a problem-solving manner.

5. When I receive criticism, do not say anything until I have time to think about it. As I think about it I will ask the following questions:

   • Is this something that is important enough that I want to even consider it?

   • Is this person a reliable source for this issue?

   • Was this criticism offered in a constructive or hurtful manner?

   • Look at the criticism objectively. Is it valid?

Summary sheets are most effective when you identify in detail the areas of your life where the issue you've identified is affecting your behavior or thoughts. Likewise, they are most effective when you identify specific actions you can take. Often the action you need to practice is the opposite of a problem behavior you've identified. In the above example, Robert noted that when he saw his wife or one of his good friends talking with someone in a social situation, he tended to barge in and dominate the conversation. The opposite behavior he needed to practice was to be quiet and practice listening whenever he noticed himself taking over.

Summary of Key Ideas

1. People from dysfunctional families often have either weak or rigid boundaries.

2. Establishing healthy boundaries requires that you:
   - Learn to recognize when your boundaries are being violated;
   - Identify what you can do in a given situation to establish an appropriate boundary; and
   - Develop assertive skills to enforce appropriate boundaries.

3. It's often difficult to hear the "message" anxiety sends because it deals with an issue that you've trained yourself to ignore.

4. People from dysfunctional families often find that holidays and anniversaries trigger the re-experiencing of childhood anxieties. They are an unconscious signal that danger is approaching.

5. It's important to develop concrete plans for protecting yourself when you are going to be around family members who act inappropriately.

6. One of the main roadblocks to being assertive is a message from childhood that reinforces the belief that you have few or no rights in relationships.

7. The excessive need for approval is a common problem for people with severe anxiety.

8. Create summary sheets for core beliefs and associations that generate dysfunctional thoughts and behaviors. The more specific you are the more successful you will be.

Recommended Activities

Continue to Practice Desensitization

If you have avoidance patterns, it is essential that you practice systematic desensitization. This is a proven method that works!

Challenge Irrational Beliefs About Assertiveness

This chapter pointed out that one of the main roadblocks to being assertive is the presence of irrational beliefs about assertiveness. Several common ones are listed below. Check any that describe how you think or act.

- It is wrong and selfish to refuse the requests of others.
- I don't need to ask for what I want since others should know without my asking.
- If I disagree with others, they will become angry or upset with me.
- If someone becomes angry or upset, I may not be able to handle the situation.
- If others become angry or upset, they might reject or abandon me.
- If I ask questions or say what I think, I might say something that makes me look stupid or ignorant.
- I prefer others to be open and straightforward with me. However, I will hurt them if I'm straightforward and open with them.
- If I say or do something that hurts others, I am responsible for their feelings regardless of my intentions and how I acted. (Common variation: I should be able to act in a way that will not hurt others.)

Beliefs such as the above usually develop during childhood. Take the time to think about each of the following questions. Record your answers in your journal.

- How did each member of your family deal with conflict?
- How did the adults who raised you train you to deal with conflict?
- What was the main message you got about conflict?
- Did your brothers and sisters receive the same training and the same messages you did? If not, how was it different?
- How did you get what you wanted indirectly (for example, by hinting, whining, sulking, or having someone else ask for you)?
- Did you learn how to get what you wanted in other ways?
- Which of these methods do you use today to get what you want?
- What types of messages or statements do you repeat to yourself when you are in conflict with others?

As you identify your irrational beliefs about being assertive, develop rational responses you can use to challenge them.

Learn Your "Rights"

Review the list of rights listed in this chapter. If any of them describes an area where you have difficulty, write it on a card and read it two or three times a day for a month. This will help you become aware of times when it is being violated.

Learn to Recognize When Your Boundaries Are Being Violated

People struggling with anxiety often find that remembering that anxiety is a messenger is the key to recognizing the times when boundaries are being violated. While not all anxiety is due to boundary violations, anxiety is usually the first indication that a boundary violation is happening. Whenever anxiety occurs for what seems like no apparent reason, ask yourself, "Has someone violated my boundaries or am I approaching a situation where my boundaries might be violated?"

Begin Creating "Summary Sheets" for Recurring Key Issues

By now, you have probably identified one or more core beliefs or associations that generate anxiety or that are difficult for you to deal with. Create a summary sheet for each one using the format described in the chapter. Review your summary sheet once a day for at least two weeks. As you identify new situations where this issue causes problems, add them to your sheet. Also, add any new thoughts or actions you discover that help you respond in new and healthier ways. After you've spent two weeks reviewing your sheet daily, put it in a safe place and take a break. In a few weeks, pull it out and review it daily for a week. Taking breaks in this type of work helps you to internalize the ideas and behaviors you're working on. After two or three cycles of working on an issue, taking a break, and then working on it again, you'll find that much progress has been made. You'll also find that your summary sheets can be used long after you feel you've quieted the old messages if something reawakens it in the future and it again causes problems.

Remember the "New Car Principle"

An amazing thing I've noticed every time I've bought a new car is how many other cars of the same make and model I begin to see. The reason is simple. Because I spent a lot of time and energy researching and deciding on what to buy, my mind identified it as important. This "fixes" the car's image in my mind so that other cars like it seemed to stand out. The same thing happens with anything you put time and energy into. Your mind identifies it as important so you notice it.

This principle is important to keep in mind when you do the various recommended activities. Reviewing a summary sheet or a rights card daily for two or more weeks "fixes" these ideas in your mind. Then, just as the purchase of a new car causes you notice similar cars everywhere you look, the daily review helps you notice when you are using old behaviors and thinking patterns. Becoming aware of these old patterns then allows you to substitute the new ones you wish to establish. In time, these new patterns become as automatic as the old ones.

CHAPTER 11

Detours along the Path
to Recovery

The path from advanced symptom control to long-term recovery often has several detours. This can be discouraging, as it is both normal and healthy to want the process of recovery to move along more quickly than it does. No one wants to struggle with the issues described in this book. Indeed, if it were simply a matter of desensitizing oneself to conditioned responses as discussed in chapter 8, recovery would be a fairly simple and straightforward process. Unfortunately, these conditioned responses usually become intertwined with core beliefs and associations from childhood that developed over many years and that are often slow to change. The good news is that the healing process initiated by severe anxiety can nurture growth and development in areas of your life that have limited you in the past. This opens the door for a much richer and enjoyable life than was possible prior to the development of one's symptoms.

Practice, Practice, Practice

While Robert was working at desensitizing himself to the areas at work that had become anxiety provoking, we also set up a desensitization schedule that included the gradual reintroduction of solid foods. Beginning with soft foods such as bananas, Robert systematically worked up to more troublesome foods such as meats and vegetables. Once he understood the desensitization process, he made rapid progress. After six weeks, he was eating a fairly wide range of foods and was again able to function effectively at work. He was still unable to go into restaurants or the company cafeteria, and he still had high levels of anxiety during meetings and when traveling out of town; but, there was a marked improvement. He clearly had achieved the first level of recovery, basic symptom control, and was moving toward the second level, advanced symptom control.

Robert's next goal was to eat in restaurants. To accomplish this, we set up a desensitization program where he would begin visiting yogurt shops, then progress on to donut shops, pancake houses, fast-food restaurants, and, finally, regular restaurants. Six weeks later, Robert was going to fast-food restaurants for breakfast without any difficulty whatsoever and was able to eat most foods at home with the exception of salsa and chips, something he had formerly enjoyed. It took another three months before Robert felt comfortable eating out, but he practiced regularly and closely followed the guidelines given in chapter 8.

What accounted for Robert's steady progress? First, he practiced regularly. One of the main reasons a person remains stuck in avoidance patterns is lack of practice. It cannot be emphasized too much; you need to practice regularly. It is the only way you will desensitize and know that you can do something.

Second, Robert used his journal to develop customized coping self-statements whenever new fears or troubling thoughts developed. The basic coping self-statements presented in chapter 6 such as "Anxiety is not dangerous" or "I can be anxious and still function," are important first steps. However, to achieve long-term recovery you need to go beyond them and address the other underlying core beliefs and associations that generate distorted thinking and problem behaviors.

In chapter 9 you saw that one of Robert's problem behaviors was excessive worry about what others were thinking of him. The description of Robert's childhood background presented in chapter 2 revealed that he was constantly teased and bullied at school and put down at home, resulting in a poor self-image. Chapter 4 detailed three of Robert's negative core beliefs: "Conflict is dangerous," "Something is wrong with me/I'm inferior to others," and "People always let you down." Each of these played a role in Robert's symptoms and needed to be addressed within his rational self-talk. Reread Robert's coping self-statements given in chapter 9 and the summary sheet at the end of chapter 10. Note how Robert is already beginning to challenge these basic assumptions as part of his rational challenge to distorted thinking.

In addition, Mary, Robert, and Kimberly all applied the "new car principle" described in the "Recommended Activities" section of chapter 10 and faithfully read their summary sheets and coping cards until they could easily recall them. Each time they identified a new problem belief or association, they created a new card or summary sheet and reviewed it until these healthier patterns were automatic. For example, Robert discovered that he often was pessimistic about future events, so he created the following summary sheet:

The Lie That Things Will Always Be the Same

Why This Is an Issue

> My childhood was a series of painful events at home and school. Both of my parents were also very negative and pessimistic. Because of this, I developed the belief that there was no reason to hope that my life would get better; things would always turn out poorly.

Situations Where This Causes Problems

I often find it difficult to plan for the future. When others are discussing their plans, I tend to be critical and point out all the things that can go wrong. My expectation that events will go poorly causes me to focus on small, negative things that occur and prevents me from enjoying life.

Things I Can Tell Myself

My past does not have to control my future. Although my memories and past conditioned-response associations do cause old feelings to surface, they are only emotions from events that no longer exist. The power to change things is now, in the present. Because I cannot predict the future, I do not really know what each day will bring. In the past, I believed that the painful things I had experienced would "always" repeat themselves. But, this is the lie. Things are always changing. If I change my beliefs and behavior, I will see a change in how I feel and respond. I will also see a change in other people and events.

Things I Can Do

1. Choose to identify and focus on what is going well.
2. When I notice small things that are not the way I like them, I can identify them as simply small inconveniences and refocus on something positive.
3. Keep quiet when people discuss their plans for future events except to say things such as "That sounds exciting" or "That sounds like fun."
4. Stay away from people who are negative and spend more time with positive people.
5. Read uplifting and positive material.

During the early part of her therapy, Mary often found it difficult to practice. She thought of this in terms of being afraid to go outside of her "comfort zone" and created this summary sheet.

Fear of Going Outside of My "Comfort Zone"

Why This Is an Issue

As a child, the criticism and put-downs by my parents and brothers caused me to believe the lie that "I'm not as intelligent or capable as others." My gentle nature, the constant teasing of my brothers, and my mother's constant warnings also caused me to believe the lie that "The world is too dangerous for me. I'm not safe."

Situations Where This Causes Problems

These lies have caused me to try to create a small, safe world and to avoid taking risks. The biggest problem this causes me at present is my reluctance to do the work needed to desensitize.

Things I Can Tell Myself

While there are many dangers in the world, I'm an intelligent and capable adult. I'm not a helpless little girl. I know how to take reasonable precautions and get help when I need it. I do not need to hide in my safe little world any longer. It's time to move out of my comfort zone and take my place in the world as an adult.

Things I Can Do

1. Choose to practice regularly.
2. Review this summary sheet regularly.
3. Remind myself of the rewards that practicing brings: freedom, a more positive self-image, more opportunities in work and friendships, and more joy.

In a similar manner, you need to identify the key issues that create problems in your life and address them in a concrete manner over a period of time. Again, the more detailed you are when doing this, the more success you will enjoy.

Relearning Is Easier Than Starting from Scratch

As with Mary and Robert, Kimberly experienced her own detours on the road to recovery. After three months, her symptoms were greatly reduced. She had remained home from work due to her injuries and had gone through several cycles of intense anxiety and anger, and moderate depression, which is normal for an active, dynamic individual like Kimberly who has experienced major physical and psychological trauma.

Because Kimberly was making good progress, we met less frequently. One day, after several weeks of good progress, she was talking with a fellow employee on the telephone and learned that a student had hit another employee. She came to me a few days later and reported that her symptoms had intensified considerably and she was again having nightmares about being assaulted. Kimberly understood how the report had re-stimulated the memories of her own assault. Nonetheless, she did not realize that they also were making her concerns about the possibility of being reinjured at work even more real.

Chapter 9 discussed Kimberly's difficulty in dealing with her mortality and her inability to control many circumstances in her life. After a couple of months, her symptoms had decreased enough so that she was not using the rational self-talk described in that chapter very much. She had been keeping busy with family activities and had put the question of whether she would return to work or seek a different position at the back of her mind. The incident with a co-worker brought this important question to the forefront again: do I continue in this position or move on to a safer one? In essence, the increased symptoms she was experiencing had two messages: First, she needed to return to the basic skills and desensitize herself to the flare-up of anxiety that was triggered by the report of this new violent incident. Second, she needed to decide what she was going to do about work.

When real-life experiences trigger old anxiety patterns, the first thing I have someone do is pull out the simple explanation and basic coping self-statements they created during the early phase of their treatment. Next, I have them review their summary sheets as it's easy to forget the skills and insights you've learned. This is why I encourage you to do the Recommended Activities at the end of each chapter in your journal. It provides a record of your work that, like Kimberly, you are able to refer back to them when you need to in the future. Although the goal is to get to the point where your insights are internalized and the skills are automatic, it's easy to slip into old negative patterns when an unusual life event causes symptoms recur. Because of this, you need to return to the basics and apply your skills in a systematic and conscious manner whenever you notice old patterns re-emerging. It usually takes several cycles of forgetting what you've learned and revisiting the basics before these skills and insights are internalized enough to become automatic lifelong skills. Fortunately, relearning is usually easier than learning something for the first time and having a written record of what you've done makes it even easier.

Kimberly reviewed the basic skills and began using them in a systematic manner. She began feeling better in about a week, but the question of what to do about returning to work continued to plague her. One of the chief causes of her difficulty in resolving this issue was the message from childhood: "I must be strong and never show weakness."

During one of our sessions, Kimberly realized that she was equating changing her job with being weak, just as she had viewed her symptoms as a sign of being weak-willed rather than a normal response to being assaulted. Since this was a major issue that surfaced in many different situations, she made the following summary sheet for it:

The Lie that I Must Always Be Strong and Never Show Weakness.

Why This Is an Issue

Physically, my father was very strong. He rarely got sick and had a high level of energy. He prided himself on his ability never to show any sign of weakness. Unfortunately, this also meant he almost never showed any sign of tenderness or empathy, since these were viewed as being signs of weakness. Because I wanted my father's love, I learned to be like him. Up until the assault, I've been able to pull this off fairly well.

Situations Where This Causes Problems

This issue has come up in a major way whenever my posttraumatic stress symptoms occur and cause me to think that I have to return to the same position at work. I've believed the lie that not returning means I'm weak. This core belief has also caused me to be overly critical when my two sons have shown weakness that is actually just a normal part of being young. Although I'm a good listener, I now realize that I've always prided myself on being stronger than most of the people I know. This has caused me to look down on others whenever they have shown weakness. It also causes me to "stiffen up" and shut down whenever I experience soft feelings such as when I see a tender moment in a movie or listen to someone who is hurting.

Things I Can Tell Myself

While being strong is a good quality in many situations and has helped me succeed in life, there are also times when it's OK to show weakness. I am not "superwoman." It's normal to hurt and have symptoms when traumatic real-life events occur. It's also normal and healthy to express sadness, pain, and fear. My father's need always to be strong poisoned all of his relationships. One of the ways he kept from showing emotions that he considered weak was to become angry and lash out whenever he was sad, hurt, or disappointed. It also caused him to pull away from people and fail to support those he loved when they needed him the most. I now see that I've also done this and it has damaged my relationships with others. There is nothing weak or demeaning about deciding to change jobs because I want a safer environment. It is healthy to want to avoid situations where you might be seriously hurt. When someone you love hurts, it's healthy and loving to empathize and comfort them. It actually helps them and strengthens the relationship. I do not need to "make them strong."

Things I Can Do

1. Encourage my children when they make mistakes. Do not criticize and ridicule.
2. Talk about some of the struggles I'm going through with appropriate people rather than always saying "I'm fine."
3. Allow myself to feel tender feelings during movies or when talking with others who are hurting in some way. I can also allow others who are close to me see this side of me.
4. I can allow myself to cry when it's appropriate and not try to cover it up.
5. Read this sheet every day for a month.

As time went on, Kimberly found additional situations where the idea that she needed always to be strong interfered with her life. Each time she identified a new area, she added it to her summary sheet. Likewise, each time she thought of a new way to challenge this idea, she added that as well.

Two other incidents occurred in the months that followed that reactivated Kimberly's symptoms. The first occurred about six weeks after hearing about the employee who was hit. Kimberly was driving in the country with her mother and children when a young man by the side of the road pointed a gun at the car as if he were going to shoot. While the young man was just pretending, Kimberly was so startled she drove off in a panic and her symptoms increased for about a week.

About three months after this, Kimberly was at a park with her two sons, her sister, brother-in-law, and their children when a small group of young men who were acting in a rowdy manner came to the park. Even though they were quite a distance away and did not bother Kimberly or her family, their presence was enough to trigger her symptoms again. This time, she experienced increased symptoms for only a few days.

For each of the above incidents, Kimberly found that she needed first to go back and review her simple explanation and basic coping skills. She then went through her summary sheets so she could identify and address any additional issues that were playing a role in her increased symptoms.

The purpose of taking so much time with these examples is to underscore two realities that are part of recovery. First, you will make relatively steady progress. Then something will happen that re-sensitizes you, triggering an increase in symptoms. Expect this as a normal part of the recovery process. Second, when this occurs, follow Kimberly's example and review the skills you are learning, beginning with the basics, and apply them in a systematic manner to whatever has triggered the increase in symptoms.

More Bumps along the Road to Long-Term Recovery

After working with Robert for seven months he reported that his desensitization was continuing to go well. His daily "jolts" of anxiety, as he described them, had stopped. He was eating in restaurants and working without excessive anxiety, and the only thing he still couldn't eat were chips. He had also flown two times with no problems. We had reduced the frequency of our sessions to once every three weeks. Then, suddenly, he came in and reported that while he could still go anywhere he wanted without anxiety, his gagging response had returned and there was not a day when he wasn't thinking about choking. This new episode had been triggered when Robert was laughing while eating trail mix and choked a little when some "went down the wrong way".

Like Kimberly, Robert was simply experiencing the normal ups and downs of recovery. He had gotten to a point in his recovery where he was using his tools consciously in only a small number of situations. During much of his day, he was no longer consumed with his symptoms and focusing on the events around him. Now, because of the choking incident, his symptoms had again become a major focus. As with Kimberly, I had Robert simply return to the basics presented in chapters 5 through 8. Robert did this and felt like he was back on track a week later.

After this incident, Robert continued to make steady progress for four months. Then another incident occurred. He was eating a steak and felt that something was stuck in his throat. He did not choke or have any real sign that there was a problem, only a "funny feeling." Nevertheless, that night, Robert was up until 2 A.M., worrying that something might be stuck in his throat. He also had a couple of brief episodes of gagging.

While these two episodes may look alike on the surface, there is an important difference. In the first episode, with the trail mix, there was a clear physical cause for the choking and gag response. In the second, as Robert described it, there was no physical obstruction that produced choking, just a "funny feeling" that he magnified. As Robert and I talked about what was going on in his life, he mentioned in a casual manner that he and his wife were not getting along very well. When I pressed him on this issue, he admitted that the marriage was not good and added, "I'm just surviving."

The childhood message "Conflict is dangerous" was making it difficult for Robert to discuss or even think about issues that were important to him with his wife. In fact, he was "choking" on them. Issues that are difficult to deal with can sometimes cause symptoms that are symbolic, such as Robert's gagging. While Robert's symptoms are somewhat unusual, they were functioning as a message. For Robert, the message was: tell your wife what is bothering you and work on a solution.

D.E.R. Scripts

Like Mary, Robert needed to learn how to be more assertive so he would have healthier boundaries. The only difference was that while Mary had weak boundaries that needed to be strengthened, Robert's boundaries were rigid and needed to be loosened. After presenting the concept of rights to him, as described in chapter 10, we moved on to a simple but powerful assertive skill that I call D.E.R. scripts.

The concept of D.E.R. scripts is easy to remember and an effective way of making your needs known to another. The letters represent the following:

> *Describe* the problem.
> *Express* your thoughts or feelings.
> *Request* what you want.

The above steps should be expressed as a short three-to-five-sentence paragraph you recite to the person with whom you are in conflict. When doing this, phrase your sentences in what is commonly referred to as "I messages." An I message is a statement that tells the listener what you see, think, feel, or want in an objective manner that does not assign blame or put the listener down. Statements that assign blame or put the listener down are often referred to as "you messages". Here is the script Robert developed to tell his wife what was bothering him:

Describe

Because I'm working a swing shift and you're working days, we don't spend much time together. The time we are spending together is mostly spent arguing about bills or things that need to be done.

Express

I'm feeling lonely and that you no longer care about me.

Request

I'd like to figure out a way where we can spend some quality time together and do something enjoyable.

The above script may look simple, but it took about thirty minutes to develop. The first and most difficult part of a D.E.R. script is identifying what you want, the "request" at the end of the script. When I first asked Robert what he wanted to change in his marriage, he listed a number of things that he wanted his wife to stop doing such as arguing and criticizing him less. This is typical. But a good D.E.R. script focuses on what you want someone to do rather than what you want stopped. I continued to pursue this with Robert. At first, because he was so used to focusing on problems rather than on solutions, he found it difficult to identify exactly what it was that he wanted. However, after some discussion, he realized that he wanted the companionship that was present when he had first met his wife.

Once you have clearly identified what you want, the rest is usually fairly easy. The only area where you need to exercise caution is in your description. The two basic rules for the description are: (1) just state the facts and, (2) keep it short. The purpose of the description is to present a problem that you are having in as short and succinct manner as possible. The most common mistake people make is using "you" messages that involve negative labels or your "analysis" of the other person's motives or personality. Here is Robert's first attempt that has both of these mistakes:

> Since I've been working the swing shift you seem to be getting more and more unreasonable and going into your own little world. You never help with anything and you don't care about anything I'm involved with.

Compare this with the final description you read earlier. Notice how in the first attempt he accuses and blames his wife. If he had said this, she probably would have become defensive and begun to fight back. In contrast, the description that was eventually developed used "I messages" and invited her to participate in a problem-solving discussion.

Once you have made your request through a D.E.R. script, you need to be able to switch gears and listen to the other person. As you listen, try to identify what that person wants. Keep in mind that your goal is to find a way to meet some of what you both want in a given situation.

Using the D.E.R. approach, Robert was able to express himself effectively to his wife. During the following weeks, he was able to say the things he had been "choking back" and work out several issues that had been major sources of tension in his marriage. The result was that he and his wife were able to achieve a deeper level of intimacy and Robert's symptoms again subsided.

Honoring Your Responsibility to Respect the Rights of Others

While Robert tended to withdraw from conflict situations, when he did speak up, he usually did so in a very aggressive manner. This is common for people who have been non-assertive. The reason for this is that they often ignore an important need until it generates fairly intense feelings. The high intensity of the emotion then causes them to become aggressive when trying to meet the need.

This was true for Robert, so he found work in two other areas helpful. The first was to develop an increased awareness of his responsibility to respect the rights of others. In essence, this is a mirror activity to the work Mary did to develop an increased sense of her rights. People with weak boundaries tend to be overly focused on their responsibilities. In contrast, people with rigid boundaries tend to be too focused on their own rights and fail to respect the rights of others. Here is a list of responsibilities I use with clients:

I have the responsibility to treat others with the same dignity and respect I desire from them.

I have the responsibility to allow others to decide what is best for them.

I have the responsibility to express my feelings and opinions in a way that does not insult or put others down.

I have the responsibility to allow others the right to refuse my request even though I might not like being refused.

I have the responsibility to listen to others and take them seriously.

I have the responsibility to accept the consequences of my mistakes without blaming others.

I have the responsibility to allow others their weaknesses without ridiculing or resenting them.

I have the responsibility of setting limits in a way that causes the least amount of harm to or pain in others.

Because conflict had become associated with danger during his childhood, Robert also found it useful to create the following summary sheet that dealt with conflict.

Conflict Is Dangerous

Why This Is an Issue
> I was physically and verbally abused both at home and at school. This caused conflict to become associated with danger.

Situations Where This Causes Problems
> Whenever I'm in conflict with my wife or an authority figure such as my supervisor, I tend to withdraw or become childlike.

Things I Can Tell Myself
> Use the time tunnel idea:
> - State What's Happening: "I'm in the time tunnel. This situation is triggering feelings and responses from the past. They were appropriate when I was little. Now it's time to come back to the present."
> - State What's Real: "I'm an adult. I am not a helpless little boy trapped at school or home anymore. I am

an adult with rights, and adult skills and abilities. I'm not going to be beaten up. Use your adult abilities."

Things I Can Do.
1. When something is bothering me, don't let keep it inside. Develop a D.E.R. script and say something.
2. When I'm angry, take a few minutes to cool down before deciding what to do.
3. Use my "time-out" to create a D.E.R. script.
4. Remind myself of my responsibilities daily for a couple of weeks.
5. If I'm sick, hungry, tired, or stressed out, delay discussing problems until I'm feeling better.

Unexpected Anger When Practicing Assertive Skills

After three weeks of reviewing the list of rights described in chapter 10 and using the D.E.R. scripts described in this chapter, Mary began to experience levels of anger that were uncharacteristic and frightening to her. She had always prided herself on the fact that she rarely got angry. Now, she was not only feeling much more anger but, on a few occasion, was becoming angry with others. This is a common experience. When someone who has avoided conflict, suppressed their anger and acted non-assertively begins to be aware of personal needs and act assertively, he or she often begins to experience anger more frequently.

Chapter 4 points out that anger and fear are the two possible emotional responses we have when a need is threatened. Which one we experience depends on how we assess the nature of the threat and our ability to meet it. Chapter 4 also points out that anger generates energy and motivation to overcome the threat, while fear generates energy and motivation to avoid the threat. As a child, Mary ignored her needs and suppressed her anger in order to win her parent's approval. As a result, she had little experience with anger.

Since one of Mary's core beliefs was that she was unable to meet her needs, her usual response to the threat of unmet needs was anxiety or depression. Her depression was due to the many losses she silently endured by not working to meet her needs. Now, for the first time in her life, she was beginning to see that her needs were important and that she had the right and the ability to take steps to satisfy them. All of this meant that she was now assessing many situations as ones where she could overcome the threat that was present. This, in turn, triggered her anger.

Because Mary had been suppressing anger for so many years, it took an elevated level of anger to break through that suppression and overcome her belief that anger was wrong. Just as she had been learning how to manage anxiety, she was now learning how to manage anger so that it could be her ally instead of her enemy.

After a few months of swinging back and forth between suppression and lashing out, Mary slowly found a middle ground: she began honoring the needs that were generating her anger while controlling her feelings in a way that was appropriate. Her anger became the normal irritation we all feel when an everyday event is not what we want. While this initial experience of anger is often distressing for someone like Mary, it usually doesn't take long a person to become comfortable with this "new" emotion and learn how to manage it effectively. This is an important skill, as low-level anger —usually labeled as irritation— provides the energy and motivation for assertive behavior. It's also a message that there is a need that we need to address.

Summary of Key Ideas

1. You may experience detours along the path to long-term recovery. This happens because the conditioned responses

associated with anxiety-related problems tend to become intertwined with core beliefs and associations from childhood.

2. Two things essential to overcoming avoidance patterns are:
   - Regular practice
   - Customizing your rational challenges to meet the specific lies that generate your negative self-talk.

3. It usually takes several cycles of forgetting what you've learned and going back through the basics before your new skills and insights are internalized enough so they become automatic. Fortunately, relearning is usually easier than learning something for the first time.

4. As you recover, unexpected situations will occur that trigger an increase in your symptoms. Expect this. When this happens, review the skills you are learning, beginning with the basics, and apply them in a systematic manner to whatever triggered the increase in symptoms.

5. Issues that are difficult to deal with sometimes cause symptoms that are symbolic, such as Robert's gagging.

6. D.E.R. scripts are an effective way to make your needs known to another and invite cooperative problem-solving.

7. When you create D.E.R. scripts, use "I messages," state the facts, and keep it simple

8. Avoid "You messages" that assign blame or put the listener down.

9. If you tend to disregard the rights of others, take time to develop an increased awareness of your responsibility to respect their rights.

10. It's common for people who have suppressed anger to experience heightened anger as they learn how to experience anger and control it in healthy ways.

Recommended Activities

Continue Systematic Desensitization and Journal Keeping

There are several activities from previous chapters that need to be continued over a period of several weeks or months. The two most important are (1) practicing systematic desensitization and (2) using your journal to record your successes, develop rational challenges, and complete the various written exercises given in these activities. In addition, remember the "new car principle" and continue to review the summary sheets and the list of rights you created.

Practice Creating D.E.R. Scripts

While D.E.R. scripts might seem simple, it often takes quite a bit of practice before a person becomes skilled at creating them. During this week, identify at least three situations where you are in conflict with someone. Create a D.E.R. script for each situation. Check what you have written against the guidelines and examples in the chapter. Record these scripts in your journal for future reference. If you find it especially difficult to create D.E.R. scripts, keep at it until they are easy to create. You can even consider past conflict situations and develop scripts that could have been used for them.

Continue to Work with Your Summary Sheets

Continue to create summary sheets for beliefs and associations that you identify as problems. Whenever you read or think of something new, add it to your sheets.

CHAPTER **12**

Two Important "Quiet" Messages

As a person moves along the path to long-term recovery, there are several quiet but essential messages that need to be heard. This chapter focuses on two that are often neglected, along with a systematic method you can use to hear more clearly the messages that anxiety brings.

Quiet Message One: Learn to Manage Periods of High Stress

Like most of the people I've worked with, Mary, Robert, and Kimberly had very poor stress management skills. A quiet but crucial message in their anxiety was that they needed to learn how to take care of themselves and manage stress more effectively. This is an important step on the road to long-term recovery. Here is how Robert took this step:

A few months after the trail mix episode described in chapter 11, Robert returned and reported that his symptoms had again returned. Since it was the first week in November, my first thought was that he might simply be having "holiday anxiety." However, as we talked he reported that a number of highly stressful events were occurring at the same time. He was working on a swing shift from 4 P.M. to midnight as well as putting in lots of overtime because the deadline for a major project was rapidly approaching. To make matters worse, a routine audit of his unit was scheduled for the following week. Plus, he had sold a car to a friend that had been impounded in another city. Since his friend had not registered the car, it was still in Robert's name, making Robert responsible. In addition to the financial burden, he needed to make arrangements to go to this city during a weekday and clear up the matter.

This was clearly much more than just holiday anxiety. Robert was in a period of high physical, mental, and emotional stress due to a number of stressful events occurring at the same time. A simple idea to remember during times of excessive stress is that your body has only a limited supply of energy. By this, I mean that you have only enough energy on a given day to do a certain number of things. On some days you can do more than on others. When you are experiencing excessive stress, as Robert was, the amount of energy you have is less than usual. Therefore, you need to use the energy you have wisely and take steps to replenish your energy for the future.

Two simple guidelines can help you conserve your energy during times of high stress. First, when under stress, set priorities and focus your attention on the most important issues. While this seems simple and logical, it's actually difficult to do because stress, especially when it's intense, reduces your ability to think clearly. This, in turn, causes you to think in more black-and-white terms that causes little things to become major issues. Take a moment to recall the last time you were experiencing high levels of stress. During this time you probably became very upset over many things that later proved to be unimportant. In order to curb this tendency, you need to remind yourself that you are experiencing unusual stress and to set priorities. Ask yourself, "What do I need to do that is truly important, and what can I put off?"

For many, it helps to make a list of everything that you feel you need to do. This helps you become more aware of what you need to focus on now and what you need to put off until another time.

The second general guideline for periods of excessive stress is to take more time to make decisions. Since stress decreases your ability to think clearly, you need to work through problems in a more deliberate and systematic way. When possible, delay making major decisions until you're experiencing less stress. Wait until you're more relaxed and thinking more clearly. If an important decision cannot be delayed, discuss your options with someone whose judgment you trust.

Robert applied these ideas to his situation and thought of a number of things he had planned to do around his house that could be put off for a couple of weeks. He also thought of several things at work that could be delayed until after the audit. In addition, since Thanksgiving was during the week following the audit, Robert decided to take a week's vacation after the audit and use this time to rest and rebuild his strength. While most people cannot take a week off like Robert, everyone can identify projects that can be delayed and use the time that is freed up to relax and reenergize. You can also look at routine things you do, and think of ways in which they can be simplified. For example, Robert decided to put off some of the chores he usually did around the house and asked his wife for help with those that could not be put off.

Two Principles for Managing Everyday Stress

In addition to the guidelines for managing periods of high stress discussed above, there are two general principles for managing everyday stress. First, develop a healthy lifestyle. A strong, healthy body tolerates stress much more effectively than an unhealthy one. This is especially true for a person with a highly reactive body. You can increase your body's physical ability to tolerate stress by eating a balanced diet and exercising regularly.

You don't need to become a fanatic about diet and exercise. Instead, take a common sense approach that allows for the occasional splurge. Just as moderation and common sense are the keys to diet; the same is true for exercise. Something like simply walking regularly can make a big difference in how you feel and tolerate stress. Plus, with regular exercise, you get the added benefit of releasing tension that helps you relax more completely when you sleep.

Second, if you tend to rush from one activity to another, learn to pace yourself. Schedule short periods of time to unwind after stressful events. These "decompression" moments can range from short periods of ten or fifteen minutes to sit with a cool drink, chat with a friend, or do some other relaxing activity to longer periods where you do something relaxing and invigorating. Remember that a stressful event includes any period of intense physical, mental, or emotional activity whether it is enjoyable or painful. Many forget that going to an enjoyable social event can be just as stressful for the body as attending an intense meeting at work or having an argument with a loved one.

Quiet Message Two: Find a Source of Spiritual Strength

The second quiet message, that is often ignored, is the need to have a source of spiritual strength. Because the spiritual realm is very personal, this is the most difficult area to explore in a book meant for a general audience. Because our culture often belittles or trivializes spirituality, many of us see the need for spiritual answers as unimportant. However, since we all must face death, illness, misfortune, and uncertainty, we all can use the comfort found in the spiritual realm.

What answers have you developed that can help you face death, illness, misfortune, and uncertainty? In Mary's case, she had been brought up in a traditional, mainstream church. However, like many, she drifted away at an early age. After discussing the need for a spiritual connection, Mary decided to visit several churches near her. After about a month she found one that felt comfortable and was soon deriving much strength from this reawaking of her spiritual side.

In Robert's case, neither of his parents belonged to a church and they were both avowed atheists who were openly hostile toward religion. Because of this, Robert was suspicious of anything associated with formal theology. Since he didn't even like the term, spiritual, we talked about his "existential" beliefs concerning the purpose of life and how to find meaning. I encouraged Robert to go to the bookstore and browse through the self-help section and buy a book that appealed to him. He found books dealing with the problems of life from a philosophical perspective most appealing. He also liked the idea of meditating and found that centering himself through meditation each day became an integral part of his healing.

Unlike Mary, Kimberly did not stop attending church when she became an adult, and she considered herself to be fairly spiritual. Unfortunately, she had been so focused on finding psychological answers to her posttraumatic stress disorder, that she had not considered the problems from a spiritual perspective. It's common for people to separate their spiritual life from their everyday secular life. With my encouragement, Kimberly began to consider what had happened and the symptoms she was experiencing in a more spiritual context. Since she had made a little formal study of her church's views, she found it helpful to discuss what she was going through with members of her church who were mature in their faith. The result was that she found her spiritual life was a tremendous source of comfort and strength that aided her healing.

There is no way I can give you a simple recipe for how you can find comforting answers to the spiritual questions posed at the beginning of this section. However, I have found that once a person becomes aware of the importance of spirituality and begins to explore it, they find what they need. While this usually takes time and searching, the effort is greatly rewarded.

If you already have a source of spiritual comfort, simply begin to integrate it with the work you are doing in this book. This integration needs to be in two different areas. First, think about how your beliefs about God, the spiritual realm, death, and misfortune can be used to strengthen your rational challenges and coping self-statements. Second, if you have a method of prayer, meditation, or quiet time that you've practiced in the past with good results, begin using it on a daily basis. If you've never tried any of these, consider trying one for a period of at least a month. It's amazing how a short period of prayer, meditation, or quiet time over several weeks can speed up the healing process and help you see yourself and others more clearly.

Developing a Message Checklist

One of the central themes of this book is that anxiety is a message. One way to learn how to hear the message of anxiety is to develop a checklist of possible messages. The model of needs presented in chapter 4 provides a simple framework for doing this. When anxiety occurs for no apparent reason, take a quick inventory of your current situation with respect to these four areas. Here are some questions you can ask to explore each category:

Physical Needs

- Am I sick, hungry, or tired? (It's surprising how often anxiety is simply telling you that you are doing too much and need to take better care of yourself.)
- Have I taken on more things than I should?
- Have I spent more than I should?
- Is my job secure?
- Is my home secure?

Mental

- Is there a problem I'm facing that I've been avoiding?
- Is there a decision I need to make?
- Do I need to make plans to deal with a difficult situation that is approaching?

Relationship

- How are my relationships going?
- Am I in conflict with anyone?
- Has anyone said or done anything hurtful recently?
- Do I need to make amends for something I have said or done?

Spiritual/Existential

- How am I feeling about my current situation in life?
- Do I have a sense of purpose?
- Has anything important happened that reminds me of my mortality and inability to control events?

As you gain more experience in hearing the message of anxiety, you will find that simply asking yourself, "What is the message?" may be all it takes to make you aware of something you've been ignoring. Until then, use the above questions to stimulate your thinking.

Summary of Key Ideas

1. Learning to take care of yourself and manage stress more effectively is an important step on the road to long-term recovery.
2. Your body has a limited supply of energy. During times of excessive stress, you have less energy than normal.

3. During times of excessive stress, you need to set priorities and focus your attention on the important issues and take more time with decisions. It's easy to become distracted by little things.

4. Making a list helps you decide what to focus on.

5. You can manage everyday stress more effectively by increasing your body's physical ability to tolerate stress through exercise and a well-balanced diet.

6. Use short "decompression" periods after stressful activities.

7. Developing a source of spiritual strength is often an essential part of the healing process.

8. A short period of prayer, meditation, or quiet time can speed up the healing process and help you see yourself and others more clearly.

9. When anxiety occurs for no apparent reason, use the "message checklist" in this chapter to identify the message your anxiety is sending you.

Recommended Activities

Dedicate a Short Period of Time Each Day to Study

At this point, many people feel overwhelmed by the many different areas they need to address in order to achieve long-term recovery. While there is a lot to do, don't feel that you must do everything at once. A short study period—ten to twenty minutes— five days a week is sufficient.

Choose a time when you will not be disturbed and that can be a regular part of your schedule, such as after breakfast, during a lunch break, after dinner, or before you go to sleep. Begin by reviewing the section of the book and the summary sheet on which you're currently working. Use the remaining time to rotate through the various activities you have identified as important for you. For example, you might spend three or four days working on D.E.R. scripts, then several days reviewing and adding to your summary sheets. After that, you might spend several days reviewing another area that you have identified as a core issue that still needs work. Use your journal for this work. Writing is a powerful way to analyze issues more objectively and to internalize new ideas.

When you come to a "detour" develop a summary sheet that addresses it. Be sure to keep the summary sheets you create for at least six months as you will probably need to refer to them when this issue recurs. When it does, don't get discouraged. Remember that it's just part of the normal learning process. Core issues from childhood that cause problems usually need to be addressed many times before you've internalized the concepts and behaviors needed to quiet them.

Develop Skills for Managing Periods of High Stress

This chapter introduces the idea that the body has a limited supply of energy that is reduced during times of high stress. It then offers two general guidelines for managing periods of high stress effectively: First, set priorities and do only what is most important. Second, take more time with decisions, delaying important decisions when possible.

Take ten to fifteen minutes to think about times when you have experienced excessive stress in the past and how you might have applied these principles to those situations. Then, think about times in the next few months when you will be experiencing increased stress and identify how you might apply these principles to those situations.

Learn to Pace Yourself

Take time this week to consider how you schedule your days. Identify ways in which you can pace yourself more effectively.

Be sure to include short decompression periods between stressful activities. Keep in mind that anything that requires mental concentration or physical activity uses your energy. Take short breaks throughout the day to allow your body to recharge. It will help you manage both your stress and your work more effectively.

Take a Look at Diet and Exercise

This chapter discusses how you can increase your body's physical ability to tolerate stress through exercise and a well-balanced diet. Take time this week to consider what you have been eating. If you are not sure what constitutes a well-balanced diet, read a book on nutrition. In general, stay away from fad diets, and eat well-balanced meals based on sound nutritional principles. If you have any medical problems, consult your physician before modifying your diet.

If you are not exercising regularly, find a form of exercise you can do for at least twenty minutes at least three times a week. Choose something that matches your personality and lifestyle. If you have a medical condition, be sure to consult your physician. If you've never exercised routinely, you may be surprised at how regular exercise can and increase your ability to tolerate stress.

Use the Message Checklist to Identify the Message of Anxiety

Start using the message checklist introduced in this chapter whenever you experience anxiety for no apparent reason. Be sure to record your discoveries in your journal, so you have a record you can review when anxiety recurs. You may be surprised at how often the answer to current anxiety that seems mysterious is something you're ignoring or something you've already worked through but forgotten.

If you do find that you are quickly forgetting important realizations and slipping into old patterns, don't be discouraged. This is normal and part of how a person heals from emotional wounds that are deep and that have been present for many years. With time, you will find it easier to remember your insights and use the skills you are learning effectively. Eventually, those skills will become as automatic as your old behaviors. Creating summary sheets can help to speed up this process.

CHAPTER 13

Viewing Yourself in a New Way

In addition to the other areas that have been discussed in previous chapters, Mary, Robert, Kimberly, found work in the realm of self-image an important part of their long-term recovery. Your self-image includes all of the beliefs you hold about your strengths and abilities, your weaknesses and shortcomings, as well as the personality traits you use to distinguish yourself from others. In essence, it is the picture you have of who you are that influences your hopes, aspirations, moods, and almost everything you think and do.

There are two general approaches for developing a more positive self-image: The first is to challenge negative core beliefs that developed during childhood whenever you notice them influencing your thinking. For example, the main negative core beliefs Mary had to challenge were "I'm inferior to others" and "I'm not as intelligent or capable as others."

Second, identify habit patterns associated with negative core beliefs and practice replacing them with behaviors that reflect positive beliefs. For example, it's common for people with a poor self-image to criticize themselves and use negative labels to describe themselves. In Mary's case, she often said things such as "That was so stupid of me, I just never do anything right." When we talked about this, Mary recalled that this was an expression her mother frequently used when Mary was young and made the mistakes typical of children.

As you identify negative labels that you use with yourself, develop more positive replacements. Mary decided that whenever she caught herself repeating her mother's words, she would say to herself, "No, I am not stupid. Those are my mother's words and they're not true. I do many things well and have a good head on my shoulders. I just made a mistake that is no different from the mistakes that others make."

Mary recorded her ideas on the following summary sheet. She reviewed it regularly for several weeks and found that it helped her recognize those times when she was being influenced by these negative core beliefs. It also helped her remember what to do to change them. As she continued to challenge these old beliefs and substitute her new behaviors, Mary found that she began feeling more and more at ease in social situations. She also found that she was becoming less critical of herself.

Challenging the Lie That I'm Inferior to Others/I'm Not as Intelligent or Capable as Others

Why This Is an Issue

> I was teased a lot by my brothers when I was young. They constantly called me stupid and laughed at my ideas. They knew more than me because they were older, but I thought it was because I was stupid. Mom also tended to make negative comments and treat me as though I were incompetent. I think that one of the reasons she did this was because she saw herself as being stupid and incompetent. Mom was also overprotective. She never let me do anything "dangerous" or "unladylike."

Situations Where This Creates Problems

1. Whenever I make a mistake I call myself "stupid" and ridicule myself.
2. I worry a lot about people noticing my mistakes and thinking I'm incompetent. Even when I'm doing things that I'm good at, I act as if I'll be found out and people will see that I'm really not that good at them.
3. I tend to "freeze" whenever I'm asked to give an opinion or I need to make a decision about something.
4. I apologize a lot when I give an opinion, and I belittle my own ideas.

Things I Can Tell Myself

I may not be a genius, but I'm not stupid either. I'm normal and that is all I need to be. I have many strong qualities and abilities: I'm a good cook; I do more work than most at the office; people like to talk to me; I care about others; I am able to help others with their problems; and, I often see possibilities that others can't see. My boss and co-workers also see me as being quite clever.

Use the time tunnel idea:

- State What's Happening: I've gone into the time tunnel and feel like a little girl trying to compete with my older brothers who are waiting for the chance to put me down. Come back to the present.
- State What's Real: I am not stupid or incompetent. I am a valued employee at work and have made lots of excellent decisions. In fact, I out-produce most of my co-workers and make fewer mistakes. I simply believed a lie when I was young.

Things I Can Do

1. Whenever I notice that I'm putting myself down or using negative labels, I can immediately tell myself the truth and use more positive labels.

2. I can take a few moments to recall the many things I do well.

3. I can stop comparing myself to others. When I catch myself doing this, I can remind myself that there will always be people more skilled as well as less skilled at whatever I choose to consider. It doesn't matter because I'm not in a race with anyone. No one is keeping score on how I do.

4. When someone gives me a compliment, just say, "Thank you."

5. I do not need to apologize when I give an opinion. Simply state it. Do not add things like "This probably isn't very good . . ."

6. When asked for my opinion, if I get anxious say, "Let me think about this for a moment." Slowing things down removes the time pressure I feel and helps me think more clearly.

What Makes Me Valuable?

One area of belief people often overlook when considering their self-image is their answer to the question "What makes a person valuable?" Everyone has absorbed from their family and the culture in which they were raised a set of beliefs about what gives value to a person. However, most only rarely, if ever, think about this consciously.

Chapter 9 describes Kimberly's struggle to accept that she was a normal person who had experienced an abnormal situation. This was actually the first step in changing her self-image. Chapter 11 described her efforts to challenge the core belief that she always had to be strong and never show weakness. While Kimberly was growing up, her father's scorn of weakness and his praise of her whenever she was strong taught her that being strong was a trait that gave a person value. Her summary sheet (shown in Chapter 11) became her first step in dealing with the issue of what made her valuable.

Kimberly's belief that one has value when being strong is only a variation on the general theme that you only have worth when you do something valuable. This idea comes from several sources. In our culture, athletes, actors, politicians, and others who succeed are rewarded with money and praise. In movies and television programs, the person who is the strongest, most clever, or most successful is often cast as the hero. Even heroes who are inept redeem themselves by doing something wonderful. Clearly, our culture places a tremendous value on achievement and looks down on those who fail.

In addition to the cultural messages, Mary, Robert, and Kimberly also received this message from their parents. All three were raised in homes where there was at least one parent who constantly criticized their efforts. They only received approval from this parent when they performed in a manner deemed acceptable by the parent. This gave the message that they had value and were worthy of love only if they performed correctly. When a parent, like Kimberly's father, is perfectionistic and demanding, it amplifies this message.

Like most who are suffering from anxiety, Mary, Robert, and Kimberly found that it was important is to make conscious decisions about what gives them value. This task returns us to the realm of spiritual/existential beliefs.

In chapter 12, Mary and Kimberly both found the answers to their spiritual needs in their churches, while Robert took a philosophical approach. Because Robert was having difficulty in defining what he believed, he struggled the most with this task. However, after much thought, he began to develop rational challenges that were satisfying for him. Here is the summary sheet that Robert developed.

What Makes Me Valuable?

Why This Is an Issue

My parents were very critical and put me down a lot when I was young. Because of this, I came to believe that I was worthless and would only be seen as valuable if I did something worthwhile. This is a lie.

Ideas I Can Use to See Myself as Valuable

My value as a person is a separate issue from the value of the activities I do. Equating worth with achievement is an arbitrary value system for which there is no objective support. I am a human being who does various activities. I am not those activities. While my activities may or may not be valuable, they do not add or subtract from my value as a person.

How I live is more important than what I do. Enjoy the "doing" and the destination will take care of itself. The journey is more important than the destination.

I work to improve myself because of the joy and fulfillment it brings—not because it will somehow make me a better person.

In order to have healthy, satisfying long-term relationships, who I am as a person is far more important than what I do.

At the end of my life, the lives that I've touched and the relationships I've enjoyed will be more important than the things I've done.

The summary sheets Mary and Kimberly developed were very different from Robert's as they focused on answers that came from their faith. Since Mary's and Kimberly's summary sheets were similar, only Mary's is included.

What Makes Me Valuable?

Why This Is an Issue

My brothers were constantly putting me down and making fun of everything I did. My parents did little to stop this and offered me little encouragement of their own. Because of this I came to believe that I couldn't do anything correctly and was inferior to others. This caused me to see myself as having no value. This is not true. I am just as valuable and capable as anyone else.

Ideas I Can Use to See Myself as Valuable

I am God's child. He loves and values me because I am His creation, not because of what I've done. Indeed, here is how God sees me:

"See what great love the Father has lavished on us, that we should be called children of God!" (1 John 3:1)

"For God so loved the world that he gave his one and only Son, that whoever believes in him shall not perish but have eternal life. For God did not send his Son into the world to condemn the world, but to save the world through him. (John 3:16–17)

"Don't you know that you yourselves are God's temple and that God's Spirit lives in you? If anyone destroys God's temple, God will destroy him; for God's temple is sacred, and you are that temple." (1 Cor. 3:16)

Notice how Mary used Bible verses that were important to her. I have found it useful for those with strong religious ties to incorporate key verses from their religious texts into their rational challenges. If a person practices daily prayer or meditation, I also encourage them to devote a portion of this time to look at the lies from childhood that still haunt them from a spiritual perspective.

As you create your own summary sheets, keep in mind that you are the only one who is going to read them. Put down anything that helps you challenge the lies that have held you captive since childhood. Make your summary sheet a living, working document that grows and develops as your understanding of yourself and the world evolves.

Perfectionism

Perfectionism is a trait that affects how you view yourself and is a frequent trait in those suffering from severe anxiety. It is the tendency to be displeased with anything that is not perfect (meaning that there are no flaws or errors) or that does not meet extremely high standards. This type of perfectionism is driven by the irrational belief that perfection is possible. A person with this trait tends to exaggerate the importance of common, everyday mistakes. Associating your value with achievement can contribute to perfectionism. Since I've already discussed the need to redefine what makes you valuable, this section will focus on the irrational beliefs that "perfection is possible" and "mistakes are terrible."

Mary, Robert, and Kimberly were all raised by parents who were themselves, perfectionists. Robert's and Kimberly's parents were much more extreme than Mary's, so their struggle with perfectionism was more difficult than hers. While I worked with all three, the first step was to identify times when perfectionism was a hidden source of increased symptoms or inappropriate behavior. The next step was to create statements that challenged perfectionistic thinking and to identify new behaviors that could be substituted for old ones. Here is the summary sheet Robert created to challenge the idea that perfection is possible.

Perfectionism: Challenging the Lie that Perfection Is Possible

Why This Is an Issue.

My dad and mother were both very critical. It was rare when they said I did something well. I grew up knowing that my parents would only accept perfection. Anything less was met with disapproval.

Situations Where This Causes Problems.

1. At dinners, work, and in other social situations, I often focus on things that don't meet my perfectionistic standards.
2. In situations where I've made a mistake of some kind, I go on and on about how awful it is.
3. In situations where I don't understand something, whether it is something simple like a business form or the behavior of someone, I go on and on about what should happen.

Things I Can Tell Myself

Perfection is by definition impossible to achieve. Humans never do anything perfectly. There is always room for improvement. If my goal is perfection, I've guaranteed failure. Remember that perfection is a direction, not a place. While I can strive to do things well, they'll never be perfect.

Things I Can Do

1. Take time to focus on the positive aspects of what I have done instead of dwelling on what's wrong.

2. When I catch myself nit-picking, stop and find something positive to comment on.
3. Practice seeing what's positive in the things others do and tell them. Say less about what is wrong.
4. Practice giving compliments and building others up. Become an encourager rather than a discourager.

Exaggerating the Importance of Mistakes

Perfectionism probably generates the most problems when it causes a person to exaggerate the importance of mistakes. When Mary and Robert made a mistake of some kind, they would become so focused on the mistake that they failed to seek a solution that would correct the mistake in a logical, step-by-step manner. In developing an approach to address their exaggeration of mistakes, they needed to address two issues.

First, they needed to develop self-talk that helped them to stop focusing on the problem and focus on the solution. Then, they needed to adopt a systematic approach to solving the many problems that mistakes create. Here is the summary sheet Robert developed for mistakes. Since this was related to the issue of Perfectionism, he kept these two sheets together.

Perfectionism: Challenging the Lie That Mistakes Are Terrible

Why This Is an Issue

It was rare when my parent's said I did something well. Most of the time, they would focus on some little mistake or imperfection. These were usually things that were normal for a child my age. In school, I had a hard time, and the kids and teachers often made fun of me. I became terrified of making a mistake because of the pain and embarrassment it might cause.

Situations Where This Creates Problems

1. I tend to go on and on about how terrible a mistake is or how stupid I am for making it.
2. I usually become very angry when I notice that something is not right.
3. I begin to act like my parents. I blame others for my mistakes and say hurtful things that are not true.

Things I Can Tell Myself

1. Remember that making a mistake or failing at a task doesn't make me a failure. My worth as a person has nothing to do with what I do.
2. The truth is that most mistakes are unimportant. They happen all the time. Ask yourself, "Is this error going to be a major life-changing event? Will it be important a week or a month from now?"
3. Mistakes are a natural part of the learning process.
4. Mistakes are gifts of wisdom.
5. Quit focusing on how terrible the mistake was and use the three-step problem-solving approach.

Things I Can Do—Use the Three-Step Problem Solving Approach

1. What happened?
2. Can it be corrected? If so, how? If not, move on.
3. What have I learned from this? Is there any way I can avoid making this mistake in the future? Keep in mind that there are some things that you can't prepare for or prevent.

Learning to "Normalize" Yourself

One of the most difficult tasks on the road to long-term recovery is learning to accept yourself and everything you experience as simply normal variations of what all humans experience. Core beliefs from childhood such as "I'm inferior," "I'm different," "I'm not lovable," and "I'm bad" result in the dilemma described in the old Groucho Marx quip, "I wouldn't want to belong to any club that would have me as a member." Likewise, many of those suffering from anxiety begin to believe that anything associated with them cannot be healthy.

To illustrate this tendency, I often say, "Did you know that talking to yourself is a sign of mental health?" I'll then ask them, "Do you know how I know this is true?" As they look at me with a perplexed expression, I say, "I know this because I talk to myself, and I'm an expert on mental health." In a similar manner, you need to simply declare yourself normal. Part of being normal is having a few little quirks, which are no big deal. Look around. Notice the amazing variety of ways in which people are created and the amazing number of ways in which they adapt to and go through life. You probably view most of these differences as normal and not as signs of pathology. It's time for you to begin to view yourself in the same way.

A common mistake that prevents people from seeing themselves as normal is confusing normal with perfect. Like Mary or Robert, those with a core belief that they are inferior in some way, often try to make up for it through perfectionism. If you can act "good enough" or do something "worthwhile enough," you can become acceptable. However, the unrealistic expectations associated with perfectionism cause you to see your actions and accomplishments as inadequate. This, in turn, reinforces the core belief that you are inferior.

Kimberly provides a good example of someone confusing normalcy with perfection. The unrealistic standards of her father taught Kimberly that only perfection was acceptable. This caused her to see her posttraumatic stress reaction as a major failure rather than as a normal response to an abnormal situation.

The force that drives the confusion of perfection with normalcy is the desire to be accepted by others. Mary, Robert, and

Kimberly all had developed a core belief that others expected them to be perfect and that anything less would cause rejection. This false belief came from their childhood experiences of rejection by perfectionistic parents.

I mentioned earlier that seeing anxiety as simply a message about a need you are ignoring is one of the keys to long-term recovery. The second is learning to see yourself as a normal person. I sometimes refer to this as "normalizing" yourself.

A normal human is not perfect. Everyone has weaknesses and regularly makes mistakes. If you have a sensitive body you will experience more physical reactions to stress than someone with a less sensitive body. This is a normal variation just like some can tolerate cold better than others. In fact, in chapter 5 I pointed out that sensitivity is a valuable quality that makes you more empathetic and intuitive than those with less sensitive bodies. This is something that makes you a good partner, parent, and friend. It's also one of the things that cause others to be attracted to you.

The only downside to a sensitive body is that when stressed, it experiences more symptoms than others. This means that you need to take care of issues in your life as they come up and not bury them. Once you learn this, it's a blessing as you find yourself dealing with life as it happens in a more direct and satisfying way.

Summary of Key Ideas

1. Long-term recovery often requires the development of a more positive self-image.
2. The two main approaches for developing a more positive self-image are (1) challenging negative core beliefs that developed during childhood and (2) identifying habit patterns associated with negative core beliefs and practicing new, opposite behaviors.

3. An important part of reworking your self-image is examining your beliefs about what makes you valuable.

4. Two lies that help maintain perfectionism are (1) "Perfection is possible" and (2) "all mistakes are terrible."

5. Learn to "normalize" yourself.

Recommended Activities

Develop Summary Sheets Dealing with the Topics in This Chapter

This chapter discussed several core issues that can be associated with severe anxiety. Develop summary sheets for any that apply to you. Be sure to include all four parts as discussed in chapter 10. In addition, take one or two days to review the summary sheets you prepared while working on previous chapters.

If you have not yet tried to create a summary sheet, I encourage you to do so now. This is a powerful tool.

Continue Desensitization and Keeping a Journal

Plan to continue working on these two key activities for several more months.

"Normalize" Yourself

Take some time to think about how you view yourself. If you have thoughts about being different from others, use the ideas in this chapter to begin seeing yourself as simply a normal variation in how people are. You may even want to create a summary sheet on "being normal".

CHAPTER **14**

Final Steps

In the last few chapters, you've seen many of the ups and downs that Mary, Robert, and Kimberly went through as they moved toward long-term recovery. Although I've described the main detours each one took, I would have to add several more chapters in order to describe the additional detours that were variations of the ones already detailed. For example, chapter 11 describes two recurrences of Robert's gagging response. After these, there were two more incidents, several months apart. As with the episode where Robert needed to set limits with his wife, each of these two additional incidents were triggered by situations where Robert needed to speak up and set limits. One episode involved his work and the other child custody issues with his first wife. Each time, we went through the same set of ideas described in chapter 11, then decided what actions he needed to take. After identifying the message and developing a plan of action, he was soon doing well again.

A year after our final session, I spoke with Robert and he reported that he had no further recurrence of the gagging response and was eating whatever he wanted. This does not mean that he never experienced high levels of anxiety. Because of the nature of his work and who he is, Robert would occasionally experience some body symptoms, usually related to presentations and deadlines. However, he now saw these as a normal response to stressful situations. He used his stress management skills and didn't pay much attention to the anxiety he would experience. In fact, he remarked that he now notices how his fellow workers respond during times of high stress; and, how he finds that he handles those times much better they do. As he so aptly put it, "I'm now an expert at how to handle stress."

During the year and a half that I worked with Mary, she also had several experiences that were similar to those described in previous chapters. Although it took her an additional year of desensitization on her own after we concluded our work together, she is also now able to run wherever she wishes and to travel freely. As with Robert, she finds that when she experiences intense anxiety, it is always related to stressful events. She is no longer frightened by anxiety and, like Robert, she uses the skills she has learned to manage her anxiety and deal with the issues generating it.

Kimberly and I worked together for about a year. Unfortunately, during that time she also experienced several more everyday situations that triggered a recurrence of her posttraumatic stress symptoms. Toward the end of her therapy, she decided to go into a different line of work that required a move to a different city. About a year after our last session she sent me a letter saying that she was enjoying her new job and has had no further symptoms.

Where Do I Go from Here?

One of the things I hope you have come to understand is that long-term recovery takes time. The more childhood issues that have become intertwined with your symptoms, the longer recovery will take. Because the message that anxiety is sending may be difficult to understand at first, you may need to retrace your steps. This is normal and is part of the healing processes.

Since repetition is the key to success, I encourage you to read through this book again slowly and deliberately. Because the concepts and skills presented in the chapters are interconnected, it's easy to miss some or much of what is presented the first time you read them. Full mastery of a concept or skill presented in an earlier chapter often requires the mastery of concepts and skills presented in later chapters. Now that you have studied the ideas and practiced the skills in the later chapters, you have an increased ability to apply those that were presented in the earlier ones. Many will find that working through the book a third time is very beneficial.

What If I'm Feeling Stuck?

It's common for some to find it difficult to work through a book such as this. If this is true for you, you may find it helpful to find a study partner or group of people who can help you stay motivated, and use the chapters as they are intended to be used.

If you're feeling really stuck, you might want to consider working with a therapist who is skilled with anxiety-related problems. A good therapist can help you become aware of and work through "blind spots" that you missed because they were associated with especially painful issues. Use the Guidelines for Selecting a Therapist given in appendix 1 to make sure you find someone who specializes in anxiety-related problems.

Occasionally someone has a specific situation, place, or memory that triggers an emotional response that is so intense it overwhelms the types of cognitive-behavioral techniques described in this book. Examples would be an intersection where an accident occurred, speaking with an especially threatening parent or memories of a rape, mugging, or childhood trauma that produces intense anxiety. When this is the case, I have found an approach called Eye Movement Desensitization and Reprocessing (EMDR) to be very useful. See appendix 1 for more information on finding a skilled therapist for more information about this.

Applying Your Skills to Other Areas of Your Life

One of the things you'll find in the months ahead is that the skills and insights you've gained are useful in many areas of your life that are unrelated to anxiety. For example, as Robert moved into long-term recovery, he began to realize that part of the dissatisfaction he felt in his marriage came from his difficulty with intimacy. He often felt distant from his wife and frequently spoiled good times by starting fights with her over trivial matters. The force behind this was the core belief: "Intimacy is dangerous." Here is how Robert applied the idea of summary sheets to this issue.

Becoming Friends with Intimacy

Why This Is an Issue

My mother and father did not know how to be intimate in a positive way. Throughout my childhood we only connected in negative ways: put-downs, blaming, and fighting. For much of my life, I've used these same ways to connect with others. In the past, whenever I allowed myself to be vulnerable, I got stomped on.

Situations Where This Creates Problems

1. I pick on my wife and friends, pointing out negative habits and often putting them down.
2. I often act childish and make unreasonable demands.
3. I often experience irrational anger when my wife does something that shows caring.
4. I often blame my wife for things that have nothing to do with her.

Things I Can Tell Myself

Use the time tunnel idea:
1. State What's Happening: I've gone into the time tunnel and become a child in my parents' home.
2. State What's Real: My wife is not my mother. I am not a child. I am an adult who is able to protect himself and be safe. My wife is capable of honest communication; my parents are not. My wife loves me and would not willingly do anything to hurt me. While my parents are not safe, my wife is safe. I can be vulnerable and intimate in positive ways with her.

Things I Can Do
1. When I start to feel angry, take a timeout. Leave the room where she is and take time to get out of the time tunnel by using the above rational self-talk.
2. When I'm feeling angry or irritated, identify what I need. Three needs that often generate old family patterns are:
    *   I have been disappointed by something or have had a hard day and simply need reassurance. Ask for a hug or time to sit with her.
    *   I have been hurt by something she has done. Keep in mind that this is often unintentional and she is often not aware that what she has done has hurt me.
    *   I need to ask for something that is difficult for me to talk about.
3. After I've identified what I need, construct a D.E.R. script and speak up. Be honest and direct. Remember my responsibilities and be kind.

Robert used the above summary sheet for several months. At first, he read it every day for three weeks. Then, each time an episode occurred where he repeated his old patterns, he would pull the sheet out and review it again. During a telephone conversation a year after his therapy ended, Robert reported that he still used this particular sheet every now and then. Although his struggle with intimacy continued, he had made much progress and his marriage was much more satisfying. He also mentioned that he went to a marriage retreat that was very helpful.

Many, both with and without anxiety issues struggle with intimacy, safety, or conflict. If any of these are a problem for you, view it simply as another area of life where you need to go through a period of desensitization, as Robert did.

A Final Word

I encourage you to continue working toward the goal of long-term recovery. I've seen many people achieve this goal. You can as well. Although the struggle may be the most difficult thing you do during your life, the growth, maturity, and strength you gain will be well worth the effort.

Guidelines for Selecting a Therapist

If you decide to seek help, take time to choose your therapist carefully. The following guidelines are designed to help you find a therapist who is a good match for both your personality and the problem you're struggling with.

How Do I Start?

Your initial objective is to get recommendations for at least three therapists. If you have friends or acquaintances that have been in therapy or might work with or know a therapist, ask them for the therapist's name. Another good place to start would be to call a therapist who has presented a class or lecture that you enjoyed.

If you have no personal contact with a therapist or with someone who is familiar with therapists in your area, ask your primary care physician or health insurance company for three referrals. If there is a mental health organization in your area, it may have a list of programs and therapists who specialize in dealing with anxiety-related issues. You might also want to visit a self-help group for people with anxiety-related problems and ask for recommendations from the group members.

When doing an internet search, begin with "anxiety disorders". Put quotation marks around this and add the name of your city when searching so it looks like:

"anxiety disorders" city name

If you have a formal diagnosis, you can also search using it. For example:

"panic disorder" city name

Here is a list of the current types of therapists you'll probably find:

- *Psychologists:* These individuals usually have a doctorate (Ph.D.) in psychology.
- *Marriage and Family Therapists:* They usually have a master's (M.A. or M.S.) in counseling or psychology. Sometimes they have a doctorate (Ph.D.).
- *Social Workers:* These individuals have training similar to marriage and family therapists.
- *Psychiatrists:* These are medical doctors (M.D.) who, after their basic training in medicine and have specialized in psychiatry. Because psychiatrists are trained as medical doctors, they tend to view psychological problems as medical problems and usually focus on determining which medication could alleviate a person's symptoms. Since many psychiatrists work only with medications, other types of therapists may be more likely to use the approaches described in this book. For some types of problems where there is a strong physical component, such as bipolar disorder, it is often useful to work with a psychiatrist and one of the other types of therapists.

What Should I Ask?

After you get the names of at least three possible therapists, take time to interview each one by phone before you set an appointment. Just as medical doctors specialize in different types of medical conditions, therapists also have areas of specialty. If you need a specific type of surgery, you want a surgeon who has performed the procedure hundreds of times. Likewise, the best therapist for you will be one who has worked with many people experiencing problems like yours.

When you interview a prospective therapist, begin by giving them a brief summary of your problem. Describe the specific problem behaviors you want to change, and explain how often they occur. Here is an example of what Mary might have said to a prospective therapist:

"I'm calling because I'm seeking a therapist who specializes in anxiety disorders. I've been experiencing panic attacks for about five years. Currently, I'm experiencing lots of anxiety. I am unable to go more than a few miles from where I live, and I avoid lots of places like restaurants and theaters."

After you have given the prospective therapist a short summary of your condition, ask the following questions:

- Are you licensed? (Many states do not license one or more of the types of therapists listed above)
- What kind of training have you had to work with my type of problem?
- How much experience have you had with this type of problem?
- How many people have you treated with this type of problem in the past year?
- What is your basic approach? How would you work with me?
- How successful have you been?
- How long does therapy usually take?

- How much does treatment cost, and is any of it reimbursable by health insurance?

Which Approach Is Best?

Each of the many different therapeutic approaches has its own set of terms and limitations. Cognitive therapy involves learning specific techniques for changing the way you think. The discussion of distorted thinking in chapters 4 and 6 and the rational challenges in the later chapters are examples of a cognitive approach. A behavioral approach focuses on actions you can take. The "Situations Where This Creates a Problem" and "Things I Can Do" sections of the summary sheets in this book illustrate a behavioral approach. A psychodynamic approach focuses on the interaction of an individual's conscious and unconscious mental or emotional processes. Chapters 7, 8, and 9, where you explore core beliefs from childhood, illustrate a psychodynamic approach.

An exciting new approach that I have found useful when combined with a cognitive-behavioral-psychodynamic approach is called eye movement desensitization and reprocessing (EMDR) or simply, eye movement therapy. Unfortunately, it might be difficult to find someone who has adequate training in this method. Although eye movement therapy seems deceptively simple, using it effectively requires a high degree of skill. Therapists often use the same terms but with different meanings. So, be sure to ask the therapist to explain when he or she uses a term you do not understand.

How Do I Evaluate the Therapist Once I Start?

After two or three sessions, take some time to decide whether the therapist you've chosen has the knowledge, skill, approach, personality, and style that seems right for you. Ask yourself the following questions:

- Am I comfortable with my therapist?
- Can I speak freely with my therapist?
- Does what the therapist says make sense and seem relevant to my problems?
- Does the therapist speak in a way that is easy for me to understand?
- Does the therapist take time to explain things I don't understand?
- Does the therapist treat me as an adult rather than as a child or someone who is beneath him/her?
- Do I feel comfortable disagreeing with the therapist?
- Does the therapist take time to establish a set of goals for my therapy that I can understand and use to measure progress?

Changing deeply ingrained habits often takes a year or more. It does not necessarily require weekly therapy sessions; many people take periodic breaks from formal therapy to practice and master the skills they've learned. They then return when difficulties arise that they cannot resolve on their own. People with very traumatic childhoods often work weekly for an extended period of time. While therapy takes time, you should be able to see clear progress. If you feel that you have made no progress and that your therapy has no clear direction after four sessions, you probably need to try someone else.

Before you switch to a new therapist, tell your current therapist you are considering going to someone new because you feel your therapy is not going anywhere. It could be that you are making progress but are simply not seeing it. If you have tried several different therapists with little progress, you might need to reevaluate your efforts. Have you made a real commitment to the therapeutic process and done the work you were asked to do? If not, return to the therapist who seemed most effective.

Locating a Self-Help Group

Self-help groups and short-term structured programs provide a valuable resource for people struggling with anxiety-related problems. If you're in therapy, these groups and programs can provide an excellent supplement or follow-up to professional treatment. You'll also find them valuable if professional treatment is either not available or not affordable. Even people who do not feel their anxiety problems are severe enough to warrant professional treatment often find self-help groups a valuable resource.

The first place to look for a local self-help group is online. Start your search with the term, "anxiety-disorders". Add the name of the town you live in and the words "self-help" or "self-help group". For example:

"anxiety-disorders" self-help city name

If you have a specific diagnosis, you can also try using it in your search. For example:

"social phobia" self-help city name

The local chapter of the Mental Health Association along with organizations or therapists who specialize in anxiety-related problems are also a good place to look for self-help groups. If you want a group with a spiritual focus, contact the larger churches in your area to see if they sponsor groups that address your concern.

After you have the names of several possible groups, identify the one that is best for you. As with selecting a therapist, find a group that matches your needs and personality. If there are several chapters of a particular group in your area, attend more than one so you get the flavor of each one. Attend at least three meetings before you decide whether a specific group is right for you.

If any of the following areas apply to you, you might also want to consider attending a group that deals with that area.

Substance Abuse

Anxiety-related problems will sometimes be associated with substance abuse problems. If you are currently abusing any legal or illegal drug, you need to be in treatment. You also need to become active with Alcoholics Anonymous, Narcotics Anonymous, Pill Addicts Anonymous, or one of the other groups for substance abusers.

Effects of a Dysfunctional Family

A dysfunctional family is one in which children have experienced one or more of the six types of child abuse described in chapter 2. Groups that deal with issues common to people from dysfunctional families vary greatly. Often they focus on a specific type of abuse, such as sexual or physical abuse.

A Current Unhealthy Relationship

If you currently live with or have a close relationship with someone who is a substance abuser or who abuses you mentally or physically, you will probably need help to deal with the situation. This help might have to be professional therapy. In addition, self-help groups can provide you with both the strength and the courage to act effectively, along with practical suggestions for how to handle difficult situations. Al-Anon, the companion organization to AA is a good example of a national organization of such groups.

Effects of a Major Illness or Physical Disability

If you have a major illness or physical disability, addressing the issues surrounding it may be necessary in order to manage your anxiety effectively. Most major illnesses and physical disabilities have their own national or regional self-help organizations. These organizations can usually provide the latest information regarding the treatment of a particular problem and help a person accept and cope with the difficulties associated with his or her problem.

Suggestions for Better Sleep

It's common for people with anxiety-related problems to have sleep issues. When such issues continue for a long period of time, they can increase your anxiety symptoms and interfere with your health, relationships, and overall ability to function effectively in life. This can become a vicious circle in which poor sleep caused by anxiety-related problems makes the anxiety symptoms worse and the worsening symptoms perpetuate sleep problems.

This appendix discusses what is commonly called sleep hygiene along with three common sleep issues associated with anxiety-related problems. It's important to note, however, that sleep problems can also be due to many other factors. For example, there are a variety of chronic health problems such as asthma, angina, chronic pain, acid reflux, and arthritis that can make it difficult to sleep. Chronic sleep disturbance associated with sadness can also be a sign of major depression. Because chronic sleep problems can be due to either a medication or medical problem, it's always best to discuss sleep problems with your physician.

Good Sleep Hygiene

For many people with anxiety-related problems, the path to better sleep is simply a matter of developing better sleep habits. This is usually referred to as developing good sleep hygiene.

- Establish a regular time to go to bed and get up each day: Erratic sleep habits interfere with your biological clock and are a common cause of poor sleep. Naps are all right if taken early in the afternoon and for less than an hour; but, avoid late-afternoon naps. Staying awake after midnight can also make it more difficult to fall asleep because many people get their second wind after midnight. During the evening, do not allow yourself to doze off while reading or watching television prior to bedtime. These brief periods of sleep can interfere with your regular sleep. If you have been going to bed and getting up at widely varying times, focus on getting up at the same time each day—this is when your biological clock is set. Getting fifteen minutes of natural sunlight soon after you wake up can also aid in resetting your biological clock. Avoid making up for lost sleep on weekends or holidays until your sleep cycle has become stable.

- Ensure a comfortable environment: Don't neglect the obvious. Sleep is easiest in a dark, quiet, and well-ventilated room. It's also important to wear something that is loose fitting and comfortable.

- Follow an established routine for going to bed: Having a set ritual such as brushing your hair and teeth, pulling down the sheets, and setting out clothes for the next day tells your body, "It's time to fall asleep now."

- Do relaxing, calming, and soothing activities just prior to the time you are to go to sleep: Warm baths, reading, watching television, praying, or meditating can all help settle you down for a good night's rest. Avoid anxiety-provoking activities such as balancing your checkbook, paying bills, or arguing.

- Reserve your bed for sleep and sex: Do not read, watch television, or do other activities in bed. The goal is to make a strong association between going to bed and sleeping.

If sleeping is very difficult, make the entire bedroom off-limits to everything except sleep and sex. Do not make it an all-purpose room where you do many activities such as watching TV, reading, balancing the checkbook or exercising.

- Use relaxation techniques: Relaxation response techniques such as those described in appendix 4 are usually very effective in helping you fall asleep. It helps to record them so you can play them when you wish to sleep. If you do not want to record them yourself, professionally recorded versions are also available at www.rpeurifoy.com.

- Reduce stimulants: Caffeine is a stimulant found in coffee, tea, chocolate, and many over-the-counter medications. Nicotine is another common stimulant. In addition, many medications contain stimulants such as pseudoephedrine, a common decongestant. If a medication says "non-drowsy formula," it probably has something in it that is a stimulant. Keep in mind that substances such as caffeine that have not interfered with sleep in the past can sometimes become a source of poor sleep during periods of stress.

- Reduce sedatives: Many different over-the-counter medications such as antihistamines can interfere with your ability to have quality sleep. In addition, many prescription drugs can alter normal sleep patterns and suppress deep sleep or REM (the time when you are dreaming) sleep. They can also leave you groggy the next day. Even sleeping pills will cause problems when used for more than a few days.

- Avoid alcohol: Drinking can actually make matters worse. Even moderate amounts of alcohol can disturb sleep or create a backlash of sleeplessness later in the night.

- Exercise four to six hours before bedtime: Exercise just before sleeping will interfere with sleep. Exercising in the late afternoon, however, increases the amount of deep-sleep in the first half of the night. Even a brisk walk around the block may help.

- Avoid large meals before bedtime: While a glass of milk—which contains tryptophan—can help induce sleep, high-protein foods may induce wakefulness. Large meals and excessive fluids can also cause indigestion, heartburn or frequent awakenings to urinate, all of which can interfere with your sleep.

- Use sound screens: If noise in your surroundings either makes it difficult to go to sleep or wakes you up, there are two common solutions: earplugs and sound screens. A sound screen can be tranquil music or devices that play soothing sounds such as the sound of a waterfall or the ocean. These soft sounds mask noises in your environment and make it easier to sleep. You can also simply place a radio next to your bed and tune it between stations so you only hear the random static. This random noise is also referred to as white noise. Turn the volume down so there is only a low level of white noise in the background and it will serve as a cover for other distracting sounds. A fan can also be used in this way.

- If you can't sleep, get up and do a relaxing activity: Do not lie awake in bed for more than twenty minutes. If the relaxation response exercises in appendix 4 do not induce sleep, get up and go to a different part of the house. Do a quiet, relaxing, activity like reading a book or watching television until you feel tired. At first, some people who have had disturbed sleep for a long period of time find they spend much of the night out of bed and get only four or five hours of sleep altogether. However, this is continuous, sound sleep, and gradually expands to fill the night.

- When productivity lags during the day, change your activity pace: The most "natural" way to keep awake is to move: Get up from your chair, pace the room and stretch. Try light rests and creative breaks instead of alcohol, cigarettes, or coffee.

When You Find It Difficult to Fall Asleep Due to Worry

When worrying about problems prevents you from falling asleep, get out of bed and go to another part of the house. Then use the Four-Step Approach to "What Ifs" described in Lesson 7 to develop a concrete plan for dealing with the problem. Summarize your plan into a simple coping self-statement as is described in Lesson 7. Then go to bed and use one of the relaxation techniques described in Appendix 4 to focus your mind on a neutral activity and relax your body. Many people find the technique called breath counting especially effective. When you begin thinking about the problem, repeat your coping self-statement and resume your relaxation exercise. If worry over problems prior to going to sleep is a recurring pattern, establish a regular time at least an hour before your bedtime routine when you can use the Four-Step Approach to develop concrete plans for dealing with your concerns.

Awakening to Panic Attacks

Some people with anxiety-related problems find they are occasionally awakened by a panic attack in the middle of the night. This often leaves them in a state of high anxiety. Current research now suggests that panic attacks that occur during sleep are not due to dreams. Instead, it is thought that they are due to some neurological mechanism that is not understood at present. People who awaken with panic attacks probably have a genetic factor that, in some way, triggers the fight or flight response. If you are awakened by panic attacks but do not recall a dream, this is probably true for you. If you are being awakened by bad dreams, skip to the next section.

If you experience nighttime panic attacks but are able to return to sleep fairly easily, continue to do whatever you do to return to sleep. However, if you find that nighttime panic attacks trigger negative self-talk and high anxiety that makes it difficult to return to sleep, do the following:

- First, get out of bed and fully awaken yourself. This is easily done by washing your face. Once you are fully awake, use coping self-statements to state accurately what has just happened and calm yourself. For example, you might say: "This was just that neurological quirk that I have. It is not dangerous. These feelings are only uncomfortable and will diminish soon." If you have difficulty remembering your coping self-statements at night, write them on a card and post them in an easy-to-find place.

- Second, spend ten to twenty minutes with a distracting and relaxing activity such as reading or watching television. This is essentially a decompression period that allows your body to settle down.

- Finally, go back to bed. If you find it difficult to go to sleep, use one of the relaxation response techniques in Appendix 4 to help you get back to sleep.

Recurring Nightmares

People suffering from post-traumatic stress disorder sometimes experience recurring nightmares. The nightmares might involve scenes of abuse from childhood or pictures from a recent trauma such as a car accident or crime. The following three steps have been shown to be effective in helping people eliminate such nightmares:

Step 1: Write down the nightmare with as many details as possible. Spend ten or fifteen minutes and describe in writing the recurring nightmares you have been experiencing. Try to include as many details as possible. What exactly do you see? What are the feelings that are generated? Do the places, people, or things in the nightmare change from time to time? If so, how do they change? What is it that stays constant?

Step 2: Change the dream any way you wish, spelling out the details of the new dream. Now spend ten minutes and rewrite your nightmare so it changes into something that is no longer frightening. Pretend that you are a screenwriter who has been handed a movie script that has no ending. Your job is to complete the script in such a way that it is has a happy ending. You may start at any point in the old script that you want.

One client I spoke with was having recurring nightmares about a car accident she had been in where she was thrown out of the car. In her dreams, she would be driving and begin swerving until she hit something and be thrown from the car. The roads would sometimes change, as would whatever object she struck. She decided to change the dream so that after she began swerving, she would regain control of her car and arrive at her sister's house. She would then go in and have a pleasant visit.

Another client was having recurring nightmares about a vicious beating he had received during a robbery. In his nightmares, the perpetrator would appear in various locations and begin beating him unmercifully. Isaac rewrote his dream so that he would see the perpetrator then realize he had mistaken his friend for the offender. The two of them would go to Isaac's house and begin working on his car, something he enjoyed doing with this friend.

Step 3: Mentally rehearse the changed dream before you fall asleep. Once you have developed the new dream you want to have, take a few minutes just before you go to sleep and play it through in your mind. The more vividly you use your imagination to do this, the more effective it is. It may take several days for the nightmare to begin transforming, but eventually, it will.

Sometimes, people who have been having recurring nightmares find that after using this technique to end them, they have similar dreams months or years later. Usually, this is because they have experienced something in their life that involves similar emotions to those experienced in the original trauma. These emotions can trigger dreams similar to the recurring nightmares. For example, Isaac was free from his recurring nightmare for many months when suddenly, he had a dream similar to his old ones. When we discussed it, he realized that there had been an incident at work where his supervisor had verbally beaten him up. The old image of being physically beaten up was simply his mind's way of trying to process this new experience of being beaten up emotionally. Isaac developed a plan for how he would handle his work situation and rewrote the dream so it reflected his plan. A couple of days later, he had the dream and it transformed as he had rewritten it. He did not experience it again.

How to Develop a Relaxation Response

Coined by Herbert Benson, the term, relaxation response refers to a state of deep-muscle relaxation produced by some set method. Several common formal methods used by therapists to help someone develop a relaxation response include biofeedback, autogenic training, hypnosis, guided imagery, and meditation. This appendix gives brief descriptions of four popular methods you can use by yourself.

Set a goal of practicing fifteen to thirty minutes a day. All you need is a comfortable place to sit or lie where you won't be disturbed. It's also best to avoid using an alarm to signal the end of your practice session as this may startle you and cause your muscles to tense up.

Depending on which technique you use and how long you wish to spend, you can go through a particular procedure once, or you can combine them. For example, you could start with progressive relaxation, and then switch to Herbert Benson's relaxation response technique.

If you find it difficult to use these approaches, free recordings of this and other scripts are available on my website at www. rpeurifoy.com.

Progressive Relaxation

Developed by Edmund Jacobson in 1908 this procedure is the oldest of the modern methods for developing relaxation. It's based on the principle that your muscles become more relaxed after you tense them.

Close your eyes and notice how the various muscle groups and joints in your body feel. As you do this, note those areas that are most tense.

Beginning with the feet, tense and relax one muscle group at a time. As you slowly work your way up to your head and face, time the tensing and relaxing to your breathing. As you breathe in a relaxed manner, tense as you inhale; then, relax as you exhale. Be sure to use moderation as you tighten and relax each muscle group. Over tightening of the toes or feet can cause muscle cramps. Excessive tightening of the neck and back muscles could result in a strain or injury.

Experiment with different muscle groups to find what works best for you. You might start by tightening and relaxing only the toes on the left foot and then the right foot. Or, you might find it best to combine muscle groups, such as tightening the toes on both feet at the same time.

After you've tensed and relaxed all of the muscle groups in your body, note how much more relaxed you are than when you began. Identify those areas where tension remains; then, tense and relax them once again.

Breath Counting

In addition to being a good method for producing a relaxation response, this is an excellent focusing technique to use when you're having difficulty falling asleep.

Close your eyes and breathe in a normal, relaxed manner. Start with either fifty or a hundred and begin counting backward.

Count each number as you exhale. There will be a slight pause between numbers. Use this time to notice how your body becomes still between each exhalation and inhalation.

As you count, use your imagination. Visualize the numbers as being three dimensional or colored. You might even imagine pleasant sounds or music accompanying the appearance of each number.

It is normal for your mind to wander and for you to lose track of your counting. Each time this happens, simply resume counting from the last number you remember.

Herbert Benson's Relaxation Response Technique

Herbert Benson developed this technique after studying several different types of meditation. In this technique, a word or phrase serves as the center of focus. While any word can be used, three that are commonly chosen are "one", "calm", and "relax". Some people prefer to use a short phrase such as "I am at peace", instead of a single word. You can also use words or phrases that have a spiritual or religious meaning such as "shalom", "God is with me", or "I am being watched over".

Close your eyes and each time you exhale, repeat the word or phrase you have chosen as your center of focus. Adopt a passive attitude as you repeat your word or phrase. As with the other techniques, your mind will wander occasionally. When this happens, simply redirect your mind back to your word or phrase.

It's also helpful to use a secondary focal point in the form of a mental image that forms a background for the repetition of the word or phrase. For example, you might imagine a calm lake or a religious figure.

Fantasy
This approach is often referred to as imagery or visualization and is based on a simple principle: Anything you imagine vividly causes

the corresponding physiological responses that would accompany the event in real life. You experience this principle whenever you watch a television program or movie. During scenes that are exciting, your muscles tense. During calm scenes, they relax.

In essence, fantasy is simply "willful daydreaming." Close your eyes, breathe in a normal, relaxed manner, and imagine something peaceful and enjoyable. Since you want to produce relaxation, the only rule is to choose something that is peaceful and calming. Be as creative as you want. You can take an imaginary journey to the beach or mountains or recall a pleasant memory. This is your mind and your imagination, so you have complete control and can do anything you choose. If you are fairly tense, you may find it useful to use one of the previous techniques to calm yourself before you try fantasizing. If unpleasant thoughts occur, or if your mind wanders, simply redirect your mind back to your chosen fantasy.

ABOUT THE AUTHOR

Reneau Peurifoy holds a Master's degree in counseling and attended Fuller Theological Seminary. He is the author of several books including *Anxiety, Phobias, and Panic: Taking Charge and Conquering Fear*; *Overcoming Anxiety: From Short-Term Fixes to Long-Term Recovery* and *Why Did God Give Us Emotions?* Peurifoy is a frequent guest speaker for organizations including the Anxiety Disorders Association of America (ADAA), the nation's primary organization for anxiety-related problems. Peurifoy was in private practice for twenty years as a marriage and family therapist specializing in anxiety disorders. He retired from private practice in 2000 to teach at Heald College in Sacramento, California. In 2015, he retired from teaching and received a ministerial credential from the Church of God headquartered in Anderson, Indiana. He presently spends his time writing, speaking, and seeing people with anxiety-related problems as a pastoral counselor.

ADDITIONAL BOOKS BY RENEAU PEURIFOY

Anxiety, Phobias & Panic

Mr. Peurifoy's first work, now revised and in its third edition, was based on a program that was developed by the author over a period of eight years and which has become the standard for therapists and treatment centers around the world.

One of the unique features of this work is the way it's organized into a series of easy-to-follow lessons. This structured approach is the reason *Anxiety, Phobias & Panic* is used in treatment centers and self-help groups around the world. One of the most helpful aspects of *Anxiety, Phobias & Panic* is the list of recommended activities at the end of each lesson. The book is full of practical exercises showing the reader how to apply the concepts and ideas it presents. Instructions for the exercises are given step-by-step, in simple language.

Anger: Taming the Beast

Anger: Taming the Beast is unique among a host of books on anger because it's designed to be used both by people with explosive anger and those who suppress anger and tend to be non-assertive.

The chapters take you step-by-step on the road to understanding why and how you get angry and it teaches you how to express anger appropriately and effectively.

As you work through the book, you follow the case histories of four people who illustrate the principles and techniques being taught. The first are a man and woman with explosive tempers. The second are a man and a woman who find it difficult to express anger. By using these four individuals, Mr. Peurifoy is able to explore aspects of anger that are often omitted from other books on this subject.

Each chapter includes recommended activities at the end that help you apply the ideas presented.

Why Did God Give Us Emotions?

Why Did God Give Us Emotions? takes a detailed look at the many sources of our emotional responses and the role our emotions play in our thoughts, actions, relationships with others, and our relationship with God from a Christian perspective.

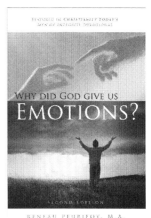

Peurifoy holds a master's degree in counseling, has attended Fuller Theological Seminary, is a credentialed pastor, and has spent over twenty years in private practice and teaching. With the gift of making complicated issues easy to understand, Peurifoy states: "From the very start, I had two goals: I wanted to look at what science has learned about emotions from a biblical perspective, and I wanted to do it in a way that would strengthen the reader's walk with God."

Why Did God Give Us Emotions? is essential reading for those struggling with emotional issues as well as for the general reader who wants to not only understand their emotions, but who is also seeking skills for managing emotions more effectively. Pastors and counselors will find both the insights offered and the recommended activities at the end of each chapter to be a valuable resource for many years to come. The group discussion questions at the end of the book also make it an ideal vehicle for small group study.

CONNECT WITH
RENEAU PEURIFOY

Here are my social media coordinates:

Visit my website: www.rpeurifoy.com

Visit my YouTube Channel: www.youtube.com/channel/ UCSCyerIGxlgSf_8-U0UQ7lQ

Friend me on Facebook: www.facebook.com/reneau.peurifoy

Favorite my Amazon author page: www.amazon.com/Reneau-Z.-Peurifoy/e/B001H6G9K6/ref=sr_ntt_srch_lnk_1?qid=1455145 386&sr=8-1

Connect on LinkedIn: www.linkedin.com/in/ reneau-peurifoy-73a20b12

Printed in Great Britain
by Amazon